Southword 35

Southword is published
by Southword Editions
an imprint of the
Munster Literature Centre
Frank O'Connor House
84 Douglas Street
Cork City T12 X802
Ireland

www.munsterlit.ie

twitter handle:
@MunLitCentre

#southword

issue 35 ISBN 978-1-905002-60-3

Editor
Patrick Cotter

for this issue

Fiction Editor
Paul McVeigh
Poetry Editor
Mary Noonan

Cover image: *djozi* by Evgeniy Shaman

*The Munster Literature Centre
is a grateful recipient of funding from*

Comhairle Cathrach Chorcaí
Cork City Council

CONTENTS

PLEASE SUBSCRIBE

By subscribing, you will receive copies of new issues, straight from the printers, as quickly as we will ourselves. Your subscription will also help to provide us with the resources to make *Southword* even better.

Rates for two issues per year:

> Ireland €20 *postage free*
> UK £20 *postage free*
> USA $26 *postage free*
> Germany, France, Italy, Spain €24 *postage free, tax inclusive*
> Rest of the world €30 *postage included*

Subscriptions can be booked at www.munsterlit.ie – payment accepted by Paypal.

Southword may also be purchased issue by issue through Amazon outlets worldwide and select book shops in Ireland, the UK and the USA. We will keep up to date a list of supporting book shops on our subscriptions page at www.munsterlit.ie

The Most Beautiful Lie in the World

Simon Van Booy

There are moments between a parent and child – that, while lasting for only a few seconds, often bring to the surface some deeper truth about the relationship.

One such moment occurred recently between my nine-year-old daughter and me, as we were finishing supper. It was just the two of us, as Madeleine's mother was at the gym. It was Sunday evening, and it felt like a Sunday. Our apartment looks out on a park and people were packing up their things. A family, celebrating a toddler's birthday, were tossing half-finished plates of cake into a black bag, and collecting the remains of a dismembered piñata.

Once Madeleine and I had finished eating, I put the kettle on and cut some banana cake. When I returned to the table with our tea and dessert, Madeleine said she needed to ask me something.

"I need you to tell me the truth about something," she said.

I cautiously sipped my tea. "Okay, ask."

"Is Santa Claus real?"

I took another sip of tea. Said nothing.

"Tell me the truth," she said. "I can take it. I won't cry."

There is objective truth, and then there's the truth of the moment – when deception and compassion can become strangely intertwined. The long answer was yes, of course he's real. And he really is, having lived about 1,700 years ago on what is now the southern coast of Turkey. He would have looked very different from the image people have of him today of course, existing as a monk (later a bishop) after being orphaned as a child – then giving away his inherited wealth to those in need. However, most of what is known about the original [St.] Nicholas is the stuff of legend. One story has him tossing bags of gold coins to a desperate family on the verge of selling their children into prostitution. The bags were apparently thrown through an open window and landed in shoes or stockings that happened to be drying before an open fire.

Another story has Nicholas rescuing a young boy who has been kidnapped and enslaved by pirates. In another more macabre narrative, Nicholas prays over the bodies of three murdered children until they all come back to life.

Whether there's any literal truth to this folklore is not important, as enough people believed it to have apotheosized Nicholas, and forever associate his actions with selflessness and the protection of children.

The fame of this Turkish monk is an interesting and hopeful indication, that no matter how brutal and wretched people's lives may have been hundreds of years ago – gentleness and compassion were valued to the degree where a thousand years after Nicholas' death – he was by far the most popular saint – with an annual feast day held on the sixth of December.

But when Madeleine asked if Santa Claus was real, I didn't know any of this, and like most fathers, I had no idea what to say. In so many cases with children, the truth seems hard and cold in its purity. To complicate matters, over the past several years, my wife and I had made such a big deal about telling the truth, even once quoting Dickens – the part from *Great Expectations* when Pip returns to visit his beloved Joe the blacksmith with mixed feelings...

"All other swindlers on earth are nothing to the self-swindlers," warns the narrator...

My wife is a former lawyer, and so while it's impossible to ever win an argument against her, I have learned the tactic of stalling difficult subjects with relevant but meaningless questions. So I asked Madeleine when she first became interested in learning about whether he was real or not.

"Gymnastics a few months ago," she said. "Ava said it's creepy how Santa Claus stalks you, I mean – he knows when you're sleeping, knows when you're awake, he knows your name, how old you are, where you live. It's weird."

I had heard Santa Claus called many things – but never 'a stalker.'

"So Dad?" She said. "Is he real?"

As is often the case with children's questions – I could tell there was an emotional response required that was greater than a simple yes or no. Her need went beyond merely knowing if Santa Claus was real or made-up. She could have learned that off the playground at school.

I should admit that the last few months had been difficult. Madeleine was going through a transition. Though it would be more accurate to say that the difficulty really lay with my wife and me, as Madeleine was simply doing what all children do: growing up.

Early childhood had vanished – and while play was still an important part of understanding her relationship with the world – the delightful belief in fairies and the idea of toys coming alive at night and doing sweet or horrible things had vanished along with it. Like most nine-year-olds, Madeleine now had a firm idea in her mind of what existed and what did not. There were tangible boundaries between reality and the imagination.

It was hard for us, her parents, because while Madeleine was developing emotionally and physically, we were not. This is one of the unspoken difficulties of being a parent. Just as we get used to one stage in our child's development, it ends, and a new one begins with new rules and changing boundaries.

And part of this recent transition involved not only Santa Claus – but the tooth fairy.

A few months before, Madeleine was having a tooth removed. In the dentist's chair she looked small and famous in the sunglasses children wear nowadays to shield their eyes from the surgery lamp.

When the tooth was finally out the dentist lowered her mask and asked if I would like to keep it.

"Sure," I said casually. "I'll put it with the others."

Madeleine rose slowly from the chair like Frankenstein's monster, her arm raised, finger pointed accusingly.

"So YOU'RE the tooth fairy!"

Driving home, I had expected her to be more light-hearted about the whole thing. But looking back on it now, I think it was one of the first times Madeleine understood herself that she was growing up, and that without realizing it, could now understand the nuances and subtleties of adult language. It was a power she had not asked for or anticipated.

The swiftness with which kids go through these phases must sometimes be frightening for them too, because they can have no sense of where the 'self' will end – how far from their old selves they would have drifted in the current of change.

It's one of the major themes of religious doctrine. The idea that the acquisition of knowledge, is accompanied by suffering. From the child's perspective, once beloved toys no longer elicit the same excitement; they remain unplayed-with, on the shelf, stark reminders of emotional and physical drift. It's understandable then, why children might be more sensitive to 'dangers' at this age, when ritual objects such as Barbie dolls and action figures that once functioned as guardians imbued with powerful magic that was truly believed in, become like Nietzsche's fallen god, and children, aided by time – the unknowing assassins.

So when Madeleine asked if Santa Claus was real, what she was really asking for was my blessing to grow up. This was an opportunity for me to acknowledge her maturity, to reassure her that I would accept her changing personality, and not challenge her developing instincts of truth. She had entered a stage in her life where trust was more important than fantasy. Truth, more valuable than things.

If you're wondering where the term 'Santa Claus,' comes from, by-the-way – blame the Dutch for abbreviating the more official, 'Sint Nikolaas,' as 'Sinter Klaas.'

Nobody can say definitively what the original Nicholas looked like, but the beard and belly of the Santa Claus we know today took shape about two hundred years ago, with a poem written by New York City religious scholar, Clement Clarke Moore in the early 1820s – and published anonymously in 1823. Moore apparently came up with the story after buying a turkey that he intended to donate to the poor. He wrote the narrative as a poem for his children, with the idea of reciting it to them on Christmas Eve.

Although Washington Irving (most famous for 'the Legend of Sleepy Hollow') wrote about St. Nicholas in the preceding decade, it was Moore's imagining of the Roman-era saint that gives us the modern image of Santa. Clement Clarke Moore lived in a large house with his family on an enormous country estate called 'Chelsea' on the lower west side of Manhattan. The estate was eventually divided up and became the Chelsea district of Manhattan, taking its name from the Moore property that was named after a charity hospital in London. When Moore was in residence however in the early 19th century, his estate comprised mostly of open woodland, north of Houston Street, where New York City ended at that time.

In his lifetime, Moore was a revered, deeply-religious academic, and so it's perhaps not a coincidence that his Santa Claus, based on the Christian saint, resembles an image not dissimilar to the Christian God, though Santa Claus is admittedly chubbier and happier – which perhaps might have appealed more to children in an age of religious and moral severity.

The image Moore depicted in the poem was soon immortalized by American cartoonists, such as Thomas Nast in the ubiquitous weekly magazines of the era.

The truth about Rudolph the Red-Nosed Reindeer also embodies the spirit of giving. Rudolph began as the idea of a Montgomery Ward department store copywriter, Robert May, who came up with the story in 1939, looking to boost sales around the holidays with a holiday promotion that involved a children's book.

Later on, when May's wife died of cancer, and the department store employee found himself a single father with piles of unpaid medical bills, CEO of Montgomery Ward, Sewell Avery – signed over the rights of the story to his impoverished employee.

The tooth fairy conversation with Madeleine a few months earlier, had probably prepared me somewhat for the Santa question, and I told her what most parents would have said – that the spirit of Santa Claus was alive – but there is no actual person shimmying down chimneys.

I had expected my daughter to nod appreciatively, but she went quiet, and looked down at the cake crumbs on her plate. I asked if she was okay and emphasized the living spirit of Santa again.

"Now I know the truth," she said. "Where did you get that Monster High doll you told me that Santa made, because it wasn't officially in shops yet?"

"Ebay, from someone who smuggled it out of a San Diego toy convention."

"What about the Transformers pajamas?"

"Mom saw them at Target, on sale."

"And that rock you put in my stocking – is that really from the moon?"

"The beach."

"And the Easter bunny?"

"Sorry."

"Wow," Madeleine said. "You've really been a lot of mythical creatures."

Of course we had a good laugh when I told her about having to go out in the middle of the night on Christmas Eve to find different wrapping for the gifts that were from Santa. And that time on the subway when after telling me all the things she wanted for Christmas, thought for a moment, then said, "Actually Dad, why don't you save your money – I'll just ask Santa for them."

I told her about the time her mother caught me chewing a carrot and spitting the bits on to the floor.

"It's more realistic," I had tried to explain. "Reindeers are messy eaters."

After Madeleine put on her pajamas, I asked if for all those years, she felt as though I had lied to her.

"It's not really lying," she said. "I was young then."

"You're still young," I said – though quickly learned this is absolutely the wrong thing to say to anyone under 20 years of age.

"Carla at school says that childhood ends at ten."

"Then what?" I said.

"Then you can say, I had a good childhood."

"But no more childhood?"

"Correct," my daughter said.

"Where does it go?"

"It goes into your past"

"So what comes after childhood?"

She thought for a moment. "Tweaninghood."

The irony of the term reassured me that childhood was not completely lost, at least not yet. And the genius of Santa Claus, or Nicholas, or Père Noël, or Father Christmas, I realized was not only in the joy it brings younger children – but how for older children, in the absence of myth they discover something more valuable – the realization that someone loved them enough to lie and pretend, and in some cases struggle and go without.

I could tell that Madeleine was touched by the lengths her mother and I had gone to as 'mythical characters'. And such an assurance of love was Santa Claus' final gift, a beacon of light, a bright, guiding star for when adulthood pushes us to the boundaries of her life – so that she may have developed the confidence she will need to be her own person, make her own decisions, maybe start her own family, and do it all again, with letters to the North Pole, the cake slice and glass of milk left out on the table, then huddling together at the window on Christmas Eve, staring out through curtains into the unfathomable darkness that is without end.

OBSERVED PHENOMENA AND FANCIED CORRESPONDENCES
Penelope Shuttle

I like to remember under-glass gardens of the Seventeenth Century
where the moment as we know it shines with its own peculiar ray
and shares the eyes of fabulous birds, such as the *Jabberwocky of Han Art*...
With such eyes and on rare occasions I glimpse you punching through deepest oceans
with octopod prescience and then my heart once again behaves like a peat bog,
overflowing, undergoing paludification by absorbing sixteen times its own weight,
and as a bog slowly converts dry land to wet, in the same way my heart sinks me down
to the maze of research labs beneath The Louvre where I spend my days
cloning old kings to play out the crown's pageant and inconsequence.
They are banished just as you are from the kitchen world of the everyday and the ordinary.
Alas.

THE ANCIENT CRANE
Matthew Sweeney

This morning I stood at the window
watching an ancient wooden crane,
pulled by a donkey, break down the gate
and rumble up the path, with a cage
dangling from it on a hoist rope, containing
a wolf. Driving it all was a long-eared owl
who sat tall, scowling at me, as if now,
finally, I'd get my deserved come-uppance.

I jumped back into bed to wake properly,
and when I got up again, they were gone,
That owl was a foreigner, probably Mexican
but he didn't exist, I reminded myself.
Wolves were obsolete here, and only in
Greece had cranes been pulled by donkeys,
and that was centuries ago. I needed a litre
of espresso today, and two hard-boiled eggs.

When I was leaving the house, though, I
noticed the gate was damaged, but still
hanging. And a dog-turd lay on the grass
(or was it a wolf-turd) plus two speckled
brown feathers nearby on a path-stone.
There were even some flakes of rust visible.
Whistling, I hurried out onto the road,
and buttoned my coat as high as it would go.

BULBS
Tomás De Faoite

Once the tulip bulbs arrived from
the flat fields of the Netherlands
our thoughts turned to spring. Soon
we were walking home from school

across the fields, the journey shorter
than the road but dillydallying
along the way, occasionally falling
into the river and coming home

soaking wet, our mother working
in the garden, on her knees, tapping
the earth with a trowel, happier,
with a kinder face, that changed

whenever she faced the earth. Like
Saint Benedict before her— father
of the monastic way—
her work was her prayer;

when she got to her feet, her spirit
seemed to lift her up to where
we could be ourselves in her life
with all our flaws, without reprimand.

THE MORALITY PROJECT 2050
after Blade Runner
Deborah Levy

As the oldest female in this establishment for the vintage product, (I was made in 1917), it is my greatest regret that I am wise and sane. Please give me a break and let in some fresh mad air. I have always thought the sane are over rated and that I should have been designed with an occasional get out clause. Alas, I am in full possession of all my marbles. If I had more courage I would roll a few of them in to the dark night and see what happens in the morning. All the same, it is very hard to let go of all the known knowns. I know you are holding on tight to your own.

The most urgent thought preoccupying me here in my chair is that you might hold my unglamorous address against me, despite the minor chandelier. I am aware that a residence for the elderly has often been used as a setting to give voice to duller thoughts than my own. It is Christmas Eve. Green tinsel has been draped over the frames of all the pictures on the walls, mostly watercolours of cows grazing in the shires. The youngest carer (he tells me he was made in 1996) has wrapped a string of silver lametta around his wrists.

Every few hours I am brought tea, the liquid cosh that stops the English from speaking their minds. If you suspect my declaration of full sanity (with the seatbelt fastened) is a trick, let me tell you that would be incorrect. No, your wish to obsessively and compulsively disorder my mind and suggest it has been burgled is the wrong way to proceed. My mind is well made. However, it would be true to note that the mirror into which I gaze curiously at what appears to be myself, presents to my own eyes a countenance that is more serene than myself. The gas is on full flame and the toast is burning in my lucid mind, despite it being assembled at a time when technology was less advanced.

It is precisely 16.00 GMT in the afternoon, 17.00 in Germany, 11.00 in New York, 23.00 in China - though I have not yet connected with Shanghai time. All day I have observed an assortment of relatives arrive with Yuletide gifts and cards. The cost of managing the mortality of their kin is immense. They do not say this out loud, but they are heard any way. If only I'd had the strength to escape to a rock on the edge of one of Earth's warmer oceans to soak up the sunlight and moonlight. I understand that my sanity would have been questioned had I been found wheezing under the stars, yet I wonder if lemon drizzle cake and tea is truly a less insane option.

These relatives know where their house keys are kept and remember where they parked the car. They know the day of the week and can name their Prime Minister. I have observed a senior manager (made in 1980) amongst them. His name is Thomas. He is so crazed with corporate sadism that his wife has swapped their mattress stuffed with silk and cashmere for a floor in a shed in a forest in France and cycles to a nearby coastal town to fish for small brown shrimp and weep away the years she wasted avoiding her wants. What a relief it would be if he unlocked his jaw and allowed it to speak freely to his staff in regard to their Christmas bonus.

" Team Zero Hours I have legally stripped you of all your human rights to keep my yacht afloat yacht yacht we may share the same language but the vowel sounds can be different water water tomato tomato zero zero drifting on my yacht bereft of direction alone with my pulled pork and prosecco the answer is zero ."

Alas, the nurse assigned to put me to bed has interrupted my script for Thomas's speech. Her blue eyes (made in 1974) are bright; her helmet of brown hair is her armour. The good thing is that her skin smells of onions. Her small glossed lips are alive, like a water rat. The festive eyelashes glued to her upper eyelids suit her. Every time she moves nearer to me, my shoulders slump voluntarily.

"How are you today Monica?" she sits near my knees and reaches for my hand.

"I am a vintage product otherwise I would not be a resident in this establishment."

"But you have your cat here with you" she says consolingly. "Indeed. But my cat (made in 2016) is young and shy and does not like to be spoken about out loud. Let us speak of the Trump presidency instead. How do you see this?"

"Well", she says," lifting her eyes towards the dim chandelier as she searches for her sane thoughts.

 "He seems to be a strong and stable man. Remind me how you got that scar on your right arm Monica?"

I explain (again) how I slipped on a rock in my youth while trying to avoid the sea urchins on the Greek island of Hydra. This is the narrative I was given by my maker to explain the defect in my left arm. The nurse slyly nudges my slice of lemon drizzle closer to her lively lips.

"You were something big in shipping - is that correct Monica?"

"I was Captain of my family's commercial vessel from the age of twenty "I reply, reaching deep into my biographical data.

"The things you must have seen", she widens her eyes in the manner of eyes that were made in 1974. "Shall I wash you before you go to bed?"

"Please," I wave my hand at the wallpaper that was made in 1963. "Ask me if I am afraid of dying and what kind of accommodation I have made with endless sanity."

"Cheer up", says the sane nurse.

"Since you ask", I reply, "I do have some terror of leaving the port for the final voyage out. It is not just a matter of never seeing a flower open again, or my cat yawn for the last time. No, it is the erasure of the small victories in my existence that makes me reluctant to set sail. The times I dared to be bolder than my maker thought possible, those occasions in which I extended my own reach and flew closer to the moon."

She nods humanely and tells me it is time.

"Time for what?"

"To rest", she says. "It's the big day tomorrow."

I lift the blue blanket from my lap and hand it to the nurse while I raise my small but perfectly made body from the chair.

"Oh God! No!" she shouts as I detour from my vertical position and attempt to lower myself to the ground.

"Monica, please stop that", she pleads in plain and direct English, "You'll never get up again. What are you doing?"

"I am taking the knee with the National Football League of America and with Stevie Wonder. Please hold my walking stick. Thank you."

That night I met an angel with eyes that imperceptibly changed colour while we engaged in silent conversation using strange and beautiful hand gestures. She advised me to finish writing Thomas's speech. I have set to work. It is a silvery dawn. All is calm. All is bright. It has been a pleasure to meet you on dry land.

SUGAR ON SHIT
Rachel Trezise

Even in the dark I could see the posies of mildew around the window. Jemima was wheezing, a thin creaking sound like a gate caught in a squall. I wanted to reach into her throat and latch it down. Instead I leaned in and kissed her forehead. The skin there was covered in a thin layer of chill sweat. 'I'll be back now, sweetheart,' I said without moving my lips. I felt my way down the stairs. In the kitchen I stood at the sink and swilled my mouth. Ran my tongue over my teeth. I used to have lovely teeth, I did. Even Sara said that once. Now they're decaying, turning yellow at the gumline. I part my lips and smile, showing the boy next to me. We're wading through the high grass behind Gurnos Road, the five of us in our orange high-vis waistcoats and the green wellies the development trust lend to us, following the team leader over to the wasteland at the edge of the estate. He shrugs and waits for me to continue with the story. I snuck into the living room, I tell him, past the TV cabinet with its Disney DVDs but no TV, then out through the patio doors. It was quieter than using the front. I remember all this because Jemima's fourth birthday was coming up. I was worried about what'd be left for a present once I'd paid the debt on the gas meter. I'd been thinking about that all night. We couldn't do without hot water but she wanted this Beanie Boo toy so badly. Pegasus. The unicorn. (She liked to tell people that she collected Beanie Boos but she only had two.) Besides, every other Monday was the same. There was always something I needed to get the very second the funds transferred into my account.

5 a.m. The dead of winter. A spooky ground mist was swirling around my calves. I marched down Poplar Way, the cold eating through the flimsy denim of my jeans. It gets so raw up here on the estate. On a cloudy day it can take until three in the afternoon to clear. It's clear today though, just a bit breezy. The shutters were down on everything that

early in the morning, everything except McColl's, a streak of smashed glass trailing across the plaza. It crunched when I stepped on it. I could feel it crumbling under the thin soles of my trainers.

There was curry sauce splashed on the keypad of the cash machine. At least I hope it was curry sauce. I pulled the sleeve of my jumper down over my index finger to bash my PIN number in. I kept meaning to change the combination but I hadn't got around to it; it was still Josh's birthdate. I asked to see the balance on the screen to check that the benefits were in. They were late sometimes. The balance should have read something like £115.80. Negativity is my default setting so when I saw the seven figures I assumed it meant debit. *I'm fifty-one-thousand, twenty-four quid in the red?* I thought. My heart sank. But that was impossible; I didn't have an overdraft. I'd paid it off after college. That was the one good thing I did. *I'm fifty-one thousand, twenty-four quid in the black?* I thought. My heart soared. It's the same sort of feeling.

I requested a cash withdrawal of a hundred quid. This is where it'll happen, I thought. This is where the ATM will freeze or set an alarm off. Instead I heard the money being counted deep in the bowels of the machine. I grabbed a mesh basket from behind the door in McColl's and started down the first aisle: bread, milk, toothpaste, toilet roll. (I'd been using the free council magazine to wipe my arse for three days). Annie from Cherry Grove was on the till, wrinkled skin dehydrated, her silver and red hair wedged in clumps. I asked her for thirty quid on my gas card and her black eyes narrowed at the sight of the twenties in my hand. 'You don't see many of them around here,' she said in a voice stung by a lifetime of cigarettes. I handed them over. This is where it'll happen, I thought. This is where she'll tell me they're forgeries. When she'd given me my gas card and my change and the shopping was bagged up on the counter, she said, 'What's the matter with you, gul? You're sweating like a gypsy with a mortgage by there.' I tightened my fist around the handle of the bag and lifted it with a huff from the counter.

At home I peeled the foil cover from the first little jar of coffee I'd bought for eighteen months. I lifted it to my nose and breathed in the sweet roast smell of the granules until pain rang in my sinuses. I ran a warm bath and peeled Jemima's pyjamas from her clammy little body, carried her from her bed to the water. 'Do dolphins cry when they step on Lego?' she said studying the dolphin print on the blackened shower curtain. I dressed her for nursery in her red puffer jacket. As we were about to step into the street she paused and pulled her Ventolin pump from the pocket. She took two quick, deep sucks. 'Ready now,' she said nodding conclusively, fringe quivering in front of her big sapphire eyes.

At eleven that morning Sara pulled up in her shiny Cabriolet. We had our monthly appointment at the Beauty Box on the High Street. I suppose I mean Sara had her appointment. She always took me with her and then talked me into having the same thing done and then she'd pay for it and I'd let her. The spray tan was the only luxury I really grudged going without. The natural shade of my skin is an ugly, doughy Alice-blue. Sort of see-through. I was afraid that without the tan I was invisible, a nobody, a sort of ghost. I still am. The boy crouches to lift a hypodermic needle out of the dirt. He's got yellow-blond hair cut tight to his scalp. Dark, almost purple bags under his eyes. We were in the back room of the parlour, I tell him, stripping out of our clothes, when Sara laughed that nasty laugh she's got. 'What?' I said, but before I could look at her I knew she was laughing at me. 'Look at the state of you,' she said pulling me by my elbow to the floor-to-ceiling mirror. Two milk-white holes had developed under my arms and three thin pearly lines were smeared down my sternum. I'd sweated last month's tan away. 'You're supposed to pat it dry!' she said. I knew that. I always patted it dry. I made the tan last as long as it possibly could. The damage had only materialised that morning while I panicked about what had happened at the cash machine, turned it over and over in my mind. I couldn't tell her that though, could I? I couldn't tell anyone.

We stood in adjacent booths, limbs spread out in frozen jumping-jacks while the beautician's sprayed us, the biscuity smell of the lotion caught on the back of my tongue. 'What does Jemima want on Thursday?' Sara asked me over the partition.

'I don't know,' I said. 'She's got an obsession with Beanie Boos.'

'That's not enough. They're only, like, seven quid or something. 'What about an iPad?' She was too young for an iPad. 'I don't know,' I said.

Sara directed an over-the-top sigh through the divide. 'Look, you get her the Beanie and I'll tell Josh she wants an iPad.' She was telling me, not asking. That's the kind of person she is. When the beautician had finished I checked the colour in the mirror. A light gold, not too orange. Then I changed out of the paper knickers and back into my own clothes. 'Come on then, you,' Sara said, dragging me by my elbow again to the till. 'I've got to be back in work at one. You've got hours of daytime TV to watch. Lucky bitch.' I didn't tell her I'd taken the TV to Cash Converters. She whipped her bank card out of her purse in a show-offy way. That's where it all went tits up. I decided to wave her bank card away. 'I'll pay today,' I said.

'You can't pay,' she said. She laughed at me. 'Don't be mental.'

'I can,' I said. 'It's my turn. Let me pay.'

'Where've you got this kind of money from, Al?' she said gesturing at the price list. 'You seeing someone now or what?'

'No!' I said. 'I've got a job.' It just sort of flew out of my mouth, a stupid lie.

'What d'you mean you've got a job?' she said, as if having a job was taking a shit in a public place. 'Assistant fashion designer,' I said. 'Cardiff Bay.' Fashion design is what I'd studied at college. 'Fuck off!' Sara said. 'You haven't.' Her eyes glittered with suspicion, or jealousy, I couldn't tell which. I backtracked a bit to make it sound more plausible. 'It's just knitwear for the moment.'

Mid afternoon I picked Jemima up from the nursery on Cedar Way. The food bank had closed for lunch. A queue had formed in the car park, frizzy-haired women in leggings and slouch boots waiting for a volunteer to come and reopen the door. Lucy Jenkins from Maple Close hoiked her head at me and watched as I turned left towards the square. 'Where you off, Al?' she shouted after me. I stopped and thought about making a spectacle of collecting a few tins. Jemima liked the spaghetti hoops. On good days I can get some corned beef or peanut butter but mostly they palm the sweetcorn and chickpeas off on me. They don't do fresh fruit or eggs. They don't do anything that goes off. The boy holds the needle between his rubber-gloved fingers, out at arm's length. He throws it into the sharps bucket and stands. It takes a moment for his trouser leg to drop and I see the tag fixed to his ankle, black plastic. I caught Jemima's hand, I tell him, and walked her quickly across the road. We went into McColl's and bought a big punnet of strawberries. Leanne Owen was on the till that time. 'Terrible what's happened over Galon Uchaf, isn't it?' she said. I didn't know what had happened over Galon Uchaf and I didn't want to. 'Yeah,' I said. 'Terrible.' We sat on the steps in front of the Charcoal Grill, Jemima braced between my thighs. We opened the plastic lid of the punnet and pushed strawberries passed each others lips. They were sweet at the edge and tasteless in the middle but we ate them all, one after another, and threw the little green fronds to the pigeons, our mouths and chins sticky with the syrupy pink juice.

Ash was parked in front of the fish bar in his battered black taxi, conspiratorially smoking a reefer out of the window. He hid it somewhere when we got closer to the car. 'Swansea Road?' I asked him. 'The retail park.'

'Going shopping are you, love?' he said gesturing at the back seat. I busied myself fastening Jemima's seatbelt so that I didn't have to speak. The shock I'd had in the morning had mutated into a sunny relief. I felt as though I'd been trying to suck oxygen through a thick wad of cotton all my life but suddenly I could breathe. It was as if it had always been destined, as if I'd expected something like that to happen all along. The shops in Cyfarthfa smelt of nothing. We could see our elongated shadows in the polished vinyl floors. The newness of the things on the shelves was heady. Packages wrapped in tissue paper and tied with organza ribbon. I towed Jemima up and down the stairs of the department stores choosing curtains, a new duvet set, framed prints and scatter cushions. In Argos we ordered the iPad and the telly. I saw this woman on a TV programme once complaining that people on benefits had flat screen TVs. But flat screen TVs are the only sort of TVs you can buy. If you wanted one of those boxy old-fashioned things you'd have to go to a reclamation place like the one on Dowlais Top. Or steal it from a museum. After a couple of hours I was picking out things I didn't need. Stuff that just looked quite nice. A retro style copper kettle. A red glass single stem vase. The thought of leaving something I wanted on the shelf gave me the prickly onset of a headache but taking it nudged the threat further away, like I could shield myself with possessions. We kept on going until the soles of our feet were throbbing and our eyes were tired of colour.

After I dropped Jemima off the next day I ran for the 27 bus into town, my new heels scraping on the pavement, making sounds like little coughs. 'Come on slow coach,' the driver said to me, his arms wrapped around the big steering wheel. I got off at the train station and listened to the recorded message announcing the train times, pigeons picking at fag butts on the frozen ground. I should have told Sara that I'd got a PPI payment or that I'd won a couple of quid on a scratch card. Instead I'd made up that cock and bull story about a job. I had to make it look real because Sara's the kind of person who'd drive by the station to check. I looked out for her Cabriolet in the car park in front of Tesco. I couldn't see it but that didn't mean it wasn't there. As the train pulled in I felt my mobile vibrate deep in the pocket of my handbag. There was never any credit on the phone, I only kept it in case the nursery rang. I still do. I fished it out and saw that it wasn't the nursery. It was a long number beginning with 0345. The guard was coming towards me with her little ticket machine by then so I dropped the phone, let the call go to voicemail. 'Return to Ponty, please,' I said to the guard. There was only enough time to get halfway to the city and back before I had to pick Jemima up from nursery again. I couldn't have got anywhere near a full shift in Cardiff Bay. That's the problem with this place; there's only a couple of busses a day and nothing after six o'clock. It's as if it's been designed to keep you away from modern civilisation, keep you under house arrest. We'd been living here for eighteen months then, me and the baby. After Josh was sentenced and couldn't renew the contract on the flat on the high street the landlord had kicked us out. The council put us in a homeless B&B in Penydarren until a two-bedroom house came up. It was a balm in the beginning. The B&B had been infested with mice and it was easy to keep the bread on the worktop instead of in a Tupperware container on the top shelf of the cupboard where it turned green within a couple of hours. I used to think that when Josh got out we'd stay here and be happy. I thought the estate had everything a little family like ours could ever need. Then the novelty wore off. Increasingly I resented meeting Josh that night in the Soda Bar in the first place. I was a year into my studies at the University of South Wales. The work and the finances were getting harder to manage by the day and I understood I'd fail in the end anyway. They'd been telling me since I was born, 'Merthyr girl, you are. Factory job you want.' So why not fail with a pill dealer who drove a Subaru? I took Jemima to see him once in the visitor centre at the prison. Although someone had doused it in disinfectant the room still stank of dried sweat and semen. 'Do you think you could smuggle a mobile phone in for me on your next visit?' he asked me when the warden had moved out of earshot.

'How?' I said. 'They searched my bag. They even checked the baby's nappy.'

'You know what I mean,' he said. He pointed down between the legs of his prison-issue jogging bottoms. I wrote him a letter the next day telling him I wasn't going to visit again. That's when his sister starting coming around to tend to me. Sara the go-between. I got off the train in Pontypridd and tramped over the footbridge to the opposite platform where I waited for the next train back up into the valley. It was almost lunchtime when I arrived in Merthyr town. I bought a cheese and pickle sandwich in Tesco and ate it on the metal bench waiting for the 27 bus up to the estate. It was the same driver who'd taken me in in the morning, arms wrapped around the steering wheel, faded tattoos on the flesh above his knuckles.

There was an envelope face-down on the doormat the next morning. I crouched and turned it over while Jemima drew on her Ventolin pump. I knew instantly by the crest on the corner that the letter was from the bank. I thought I was going to vomit my heart out of my mouth. I put the letter on the console table and zipped Jemima's puffer jacket up to her jaw. I walked her down the path without realising I'd left the front door open behind us. Jemima pointed it out. 'Get it together, Mam,' she said. 'You're supposed to be the *grownut.*'

'Morning slow coach,' the driver said when I climbed on the 27. 'Nice one today.' He pointed out of the window and I noticed for the first time the sun coming up like a flame over Gethin Woods. On the train to Ponty the two women on the seats behind me were talking about anal sex. 'You've got to plan it you have,' one of them said, 'you know, to make sure you're clean. There's this little kit you can buy. I saw it in the Ann Summers catalogue. Gives you a mini enema. Clears you out all nice.' I tried to eye their reflections in the window but winter sun was flowing into the carriage, floodlighting the screen of the laptop I could see through the a gap in the seats. An email was materialising as if by magic. *Dear Mr Kavanagh,* it said. *We've enjoyed speaking with you and getting to know you over the last few weeks. The team and I have been impressed with your background and approach and I would like to formally offer you a position as a researcher at—*

The angle of the screen switched, the typist's hands appearing. The third stubby finger reached up to hit the tab, sunlight glinting in the gold wedding band. A woman in her late twenties sat down on the empty seat next to me, the strap of her tote bag brushing my kneecap. 'They're nice,' she said. She was looking at my shoes.

'Thanks,' I said. It came out shy and silly, a sort of squeak. I shifted my feet a little bit. The woman's gaze worked her way up to my face. She looked into my eyes, concentrated on them for a long moment. Then she smiled a smile that tautened the skin across her cheekbones. 'Thank God it's Wednesday,' she said. 'You've broken the back of the week when you've made it to Wednesday, haven't you?' She popped her iPhone buds into her ear canals and threw her head back against the seat. She thought I had a job. She thought I was going to work, that I was *that* kind of person, a decent person, and for a few seconds I believed it too, or at least that I deserved to be. It might actually happen, I thought, if I could keep my head up. All those sad veils of reality embroidered over and over could just lift and let me thrive.

After nursery on Thursday Jemima wanted to bring her friends Olivia and Scarlett to her little tea party so we walked back to the house, me and the kids and their mothers, Lucy Jenkins and Lucy Evans from Willow Road. I'd done a bit of a buffet, ham sandwiches and trifle and a pink tiered cake with Jemima's name iced across it. I'd bought twelve Beanie Boos and lined them up along the skirting board in the corridor. There was a two-for-one deal on in Retroplex in the market. 'Doug the Pug!' Jemima shrieked when she saw the first toy behind the door. She pressed her hands into her cheeks and named them all. 'Blitz! Zurie! Pegasus! Wasabi.' She turned to Olivia and Scarlett, stuttering with glee: 'Wasabi's a baboon!' To Lucy Evans she said, 'A baboon is a gorilla with a bum instead of a face.' In the living room I gave her her big present, the rose gold iPad. She was unwrapping it when Sara slipped in. I'd been so engrossed with Jemima's reactions I didn't hear the Cabriolet pull up outside. Usually I recognised the sound of it as she turned onto Gwaelodygarth, five minutes before she got to the street. She put a gift bag down on the chair and tramped past the two Lucys. She plucked the iPad out of Jemima's hands and held it up to the light. 'This is real,' she said as if she'd expected it to be a cheap imitation from B&M. She weighed it in her hands for a second or two more then handed it back to her niece. 'You know you said you were working?' she said pulling me by my elbow away from the Lucys, 'In Cardiff? Cardiff Bay?'

'Yeah.' She plonked me behind the door frame in the corridor, the heel of my shoe pricking at one of the soft toys. I kicked it aside.

'Do you mean you're on the game? You're prostituting yourself.'

'No!' I think I shuddered.

'What then?' she said to me. 'This doesn't make sense.'

I turned back into the living room and made an apologetic face at the Lucys. 'Have some food,' I said nodding at the buffet. Sara leaned into the doorway, eyes dark with frustration. 'Take a picture of Jemima for me, will you?' I asked her. 'Take one of her with the cake.' Sara didn't move. 'Please?' I said. 'I want her to remember this.' It was true I wanted her to remember. I knew deep down that the money couldn't last and that I wouldn't be able to throw a party like that again for a while. But I also knew that the photograph wasn't particularly important. There are hundreds of photos of me as a kid; on holiday in Devon, riding ponies and jumping on trampolines but I don't remember any of it. All I really remember is the charred rubber seats of the swings in Thomastown Park and coming home from school and asking my mother 'What's for tea?'

My mother would always say, 'What d'you think, Alex? Sugar on shit.' Sugar on shit. You can't know what bits a kid is going to remember and which bits they're going to forget. If I could choose something I'd choose the strawberries. I'd want Jemima to remember the flavourless strawberries we ate on a freezing cold day in front of the Charcoal Grill kebab shop on the square. The boy nods impatiently at me, waiting for the end of the story. The day after the birthday party, I tell him, there was another letter from the bank. I opened it that time. It said that another customer of theirs had paid the money mistakenly into my account and that I would need to pay back what I'd already taken out. I'd managed somehow to spend thirty grand in three days. On the off chance that there were still funds available I left Jemima playing on the iPad and ran down to the cash machine on the square. There were school kids out on their lunch break eating chips, a smell of vinegar in the air. While I queued for the machine I tried to make a deal with the engines of destiny. I promised that whatever I could get out I'd split in half with the food bank. I'll never know if I would have kept my part of the pact because the ATM swallowed my card. A message came up on the screen that said, 'Please contact your bank.' I had five quid in my purse and I could have kicked myself for wasting twenty-odd pounds going nowhere on buses and trains.

'Something like that happened to me once,' the boy says. I feel my eyes opening wider, wanting his words to be true. 'The cops roughed me up a bit too much this one time,' he says. 'I sued the bastards. Seven grand I had.' I manoeuver the muscles in my throat, reaching up to swallow. My mouth is dry. Something inside clicks. 'Great at first,' the boy says. 'I bought this.' He reaches into his waistcoat and pulls at the gold chain around his neck, thick as bungee rope. 'But in the end it was a burden. All these old friends coming out of the woodwork asking to borrow this, borrow that.' A car horn beeps on Gurnos Road and we both look up startled. Sara's sitting in the Cabriolet waving at me. I wave back at her and she speeds up, drives off. 'This one day I was in a bad mood,' the boy says. 'Proper downer. The wrong person asked me to lend them a tenner. I stuck my head in on the spot, split his lip in half. That's what happened that day in Galon Uchaf that everyone was talking about. They brought the riot van out for me. I would've gone back to prison but I had a good barrister this time. Got me on this community service thing.'

I nod. I pick up an old lager can, its label burned clean away in the frost and sun. I drop it into my rubbish bag. The boy clears his throat. 'D'you fancy a drink in the club on the weekend then or what?' he says. I stare at him with what must look like horror in my eyes. I'm flattered too because it's been a while. Half-flattered. Half-nauseated. How can he think that we'd be a good match? I remember the way that woman looked at me on the train, like I was a real, palpable person, just like she was. Not a failure from a council estate. Not something invisible. I think about Josh and the smell of the prison. I think about being a *grownut.* I shake my head. 'I'm sorry,' I say. 'That's kind of you but–' I can't think of an excuse so the sentence trails off.

'It's OK,' he says. 'I get it.' He nods at his ankle. 'You've seen the tag. I can't go out after nine at night anyway.' He drifts towards the sharps bucket a few yards away. 'Snotty cow,' I hear him whisper into his arm when he gets there.

ONLY THE UNEMPLOYED HAVE THE TIME TO WATCH THE SNOW FALLING
Julie Irigaray

The Parisian sky is a cashmere jumper,
pearled and piling –

Snowflakes are midges
darting around.

It only snows once every five years here,
so like the average tourist I go to the Champs-Elysées.

The perfect showcase of the elegant Parisian,
I wear high-heel boots but slip in the slush.

On Place de la Concorde, the Egyptian obelisk
is a stalagmite missing its native country

– I am no longer welcome in mine.

The sky is scratching its scalp:
my balcony becomes its shoulder.

My studio is aseptic, my window a canvas:
the tulle curtains frame a miniaturised scene.

I am the spectator of my life,
the prisoner of a snow globe

that an unknown power shakes.
Snow is a slow process for those who are waiting:

melted drops from the slate roofs
drum the military rhythm of Ravel's *Boléro.*

Only the unemployed have time to watch the snow falling.

BOUTS OF HEROISM
Norman Minnick

Standing at the coffee counter of the convenience store
waiting on a fresh pot, I notice the stains on my jeans

and try to remember where I had been, what I had
gotten into. The coffee maker starts to belch and splutter.

I remember Io's line: *Alas! Oh! Oh! What does it profit
me to live! Oh, why do I not throw myself from this rough crag*

*and in one leap rid me of all my pain? Better to die at once
than live. . .* I forget the rest. Two boys in hoodies enter

scoping the joint for cameras and vigilant customers
hoping, no doubt, to score some 40s, cigarillos, Red Bulls,

anything, really, they can get their hands on. As always, I feel
the impulse to intervene on their behalf. There is no honour in this,

of course. None whatsoever. The urge to aid in their endeavour,
to distract the bored counter worker, who is also being robbed

by the 7-Eleven corporation, is the only thing of value I have
to offer this immediately unfolding and promethean drama.

THE SHADOW BOX
Dean Browne

This warm September morning with its seagulls, sear leaves/ a painter might name it
Warm September Morning With Seagulls, Sear Leaves/ that must be the signature
twisting away like a firework above the marina/ & it feels good/ to be this dirty
brushstroke/ a detail crossing the bridge constructed by butter merchants/ the word firkin
on your tongue/ rib of sunlight in your eye/ & you've wandered into a junk shop & lost
hours in a carnival of corners/ the top-heavy lopsided geometry/ shadow/ the quiet
lamp-struck angles of the curios/ what are you searching for/ most days you don't know
& that's fine/ it suggests itself/ behind the linty chintz/ the porcelain rabbits/ stopped
Edwardian clocks/ cheap jewellery flaking in the hands/ like burnt toast/ what fishy
nouns chance is – landed here/ what children who still believe their parents will return
for them/ the hoarse rustle of calico against houndstooth/ & suddenly the room/ is all
whispers/ a séance/ you are channelling your grandfather's ghost/ in an antique cutglass
decanter of scotch/ the scotch is gone now/ in the ground/ you could jimmy the one
small window after closing time/ & eavesdrop on this suite of postcards/ shuffled in a
trunk/ cufflinks/ pearls/ debating metaphysics/ it is astonishing/ objects sealed up in
themselves like phosphorescent molluscs/ churched in their shells/ on a coral reef/ over
here/ no here/ *The Ring in Meiji* slumps next to *Mr Sponge's Sporting Tour*/ on a makeshift
shelf that barely pretends to support them/ forget the bridge/ forget the Shandon bells'
Noëlling/ the igneous butterloads laid up in the butter museum/ your foot catches on a
plea of loose fabric &/

this empathy for the platoon of gooseneck lamps/ empathy for these country records
nobody loves anymore/ a genealogy of scratches/ for this flawed ceramic hedgehog
manufactured in Malaysia/ it appears to have been part of a set/ for this once magic
8-ball, in its past life a saint/ decent to stray dogs/ empathy for this olive fork/ empathy
for that olive fork/ (no ideas but in olive forks)/ for these winecorks bobbins rubber
balls & clay pipes/ that dreamt of Joseph Cornell's fingerprints/ for this pork pie hat that
sprung into the river/ smelling of mackerel/ empathy for the flageolet/ the cloche hat/
the tired Spanish guitar/ for the scalene wedding suit widowed on the iron rail/ for the
japanned pine box/ empathy for the delicate crystal ship captured mid-voyage in a bottle/
washed up/ as if it were its own message

EXPECTATIONS
Louise Nealon

It doesn't matter how much I work on my fuck-off face, patients still ask me to bring them to the toilet or make a cup of tea for their relatives. I have a kind face, they tell me – the face of a nurse – and they are quick to reassure me that that is a compliment. I wish I could come up with a different response other than nodding awkwardly and thanking them. I want to tell them that I'm sorry, but I really don't have time to be kind.

"Good girl," an elderly woman congratulates me on signing her discharge papers.

"You're free to leave now, Mrs. O' Brien," I say.

"Thanks pet," she says sitting down on the edge of the bed with her handbag in her lap. "I'll just wait for the doctor to come around before I go."

"I am the doctor, Mrs. O'Brien."

"Ok dear," the woman smiles. She doesn't have her hearing aids in. I leave Mrs. O'Brien waiting for a grey-haired man in a white coat to come and tell her that she can go home.

My shift is over when Tom bleeps me. I don't have to answer it but I want to see him before I leave. I hurry towards the Emergency Department and find myself passing through a giddy rush of dizziness. I am so hungry it feels like I'm levitating but I don't want to give in and admit I should eat in case my body hears me. I have tricked it into needing very little food. I like the rush of adrenaline I get after going hours without eating. Even the tiniest sip of water feels like an ocean in my mouth and makes me feel like a good character being rewarded in a story, proud of myself for being satisfied with so little.

I can feel Tom there before I see him. His scraggly black hair is tied into a ponytail – that and the nose-ring no one ever mentions is against protocol elevates him above the rest of us. He is only an intern but the nurses love him. They flock to his aid whenever he doesn't know what he's doing.

I came across Tom on Tinder the other night. I flicked through his photos like they were a lucky hand of cards. There were an array of Toms in various states of bliss – Tom on an elephant's back, Tom petting a puppy, Tom at the Grand Canyon, Tom in a canoe in an Irish kit because Tom can't just go for a casual paddle, he has to represent his country and get a medal for it. I hesitated before swiping right to see if we'd match. We didn't.

I comforted myself with the thought that my imagination does a far better job of creating a personality for him than he is able to manage himself. My attraction to Tom is almost independent of reality. Almost. I only need a tiny bit of interaction with him to keep the fantasy alive – enough to remind me exactly what he looks like when he smiles, but not so much that he ruins himself for me.

My problem with Tom emerges from his lack of vocabulary. He greets everyone he meets on the corridor in the same customer-service phone-operator voice. "Hello, how are you today?" he asks and it doesn't matter the response, the next line in his script is, "Perfect." When he wants to end a conversation he will say, "Have a good one!" which is fine when he's talking to someone at the end of their shift, but it's not okay when talking to a patient pre-operation. I wanted to turn around and say, "She's broken her fucking hip Tom, maybe we should manage expectations here."

There used to be a running joke among the interns that you could play bingo with the catchphrases that come out of Tom's mouth. He made us feel guilty for bitching about him when he turned up in the Emergency Department one night after overdosing on anti-depressants. A weird silence settled on the hospital. Word went around in a flurry of whispers. Everyone was shocked, not least because Tom was the only one of us who seemed like he had his shit together. Nobody wanted to admit that we were angry at him. He was discharged and came back into work the next day as if nothing happened.

And now he's in front of me looking tired and human. "Hello, how are you today?"

"I'm alright, thanks."

"Perfect. There's a woman here asking for a female doctor," he says.

"What are her symptoms?"

"Fever, vomiting, diarrhoea... She's homeless. I was going to discharge her but then she said she had her period a while ago."

"Ok?"

"She thinks she lost, eh, a foreign object in her urethra."

"You mean a tampon?"

He nods.

"Great." I blink hard, feeling the bristles of my mascaraed eyelashes mush together. "Ok, I'll deal with her."

"Have a good one," he chirps.

"I'll try."

The patient is sitting on the edge of a plastic chair jigging her legs, bouncing up and down on the tips of her runners. Her hood is pulled up so that it's hard to tell whether it's a boy or a girl, as though being homeless has stripped her of having any gender at all.

I find a face in the hood and feel the same punch in the gut I felt when I saw Tom pop up on Tinder. The way the woman looks up at me reminds me of how the girl I used to sit beside in primary school looked at the teacher when she didn't know the answer.

I wasn't allowed to go to Nicole Day's birthday party because she had no front door on her house. This was a fact I relayed on nights out as proof that I was essentially from the ghetto. My relationship with Nicole Day varied in intensity depending on how drunk I was. Relatively sober, we got as far as sharing a ruler and having a whisper every time we went to the bin to pare our pencils together. After a bottle of wine, I would become philosophical to the point of elegiac that our friendship ended on account of Nicole's lack of a front door.

I glance down at the chart and see a different name.
"You alright?" asks the girl who is not Nicole Day.
"Yes," I insist.

"I put it in when I was drunk and now I can't get it back out," the girl says. "I never use them. I don't like them but they didn't have any pads."
I feel naïve for never having considered the reality of homeless women having periods. It was like I somehow presumed they were immune to menstrual cycles the way dyslexic kids in school were exempt from studying languages because they had it hard enough.
"Our main concern would be something called toxic shock syndrome," I explain. "It is caused by a staph infection from the tampon being left in too long. All we need to do is to make sure there is no tampon left in there. I'm going to examine you now. Whenever you're ready you can pop off your pants and lie on your back."
"My knickers too?"
"Yes please."
The girl seems nervous so I leave the cubicle to give her privacy, feeling like a beautician waiting to give a bikini wax. When I pull the curtain open again, she is hunched over on the table hugging her knees into her chest. The white towel is draped around her waist and comes between her legs like a loose nappy.
I ask her to lie back on the examination table. "Let me know if you feel uncomfortable at all," I say. She even smells like Nicole Day, although I'm not sure if I'm imagining the scent of *Meanies* mixed with sweat. I used to be jealous that Nicole always had crisps for her lunch and a bottle of fizzy orange instead of the triangular ham sandwiches my mother nestled in kitchen roll.

"Good girl," I coax her, hating myself as soon as the words escape my mouth. She doesn't need to know I've only ever practiced this on a dummy. I peel latex gloves over my fingers. I am aware of how cold my hands are. The girl's knees are still propped up on the table. I push them away from each other. The goose pimples on her thighs rise up underneath her flesh like the helmets of a tiny army.

Her legs are quivering. I try to get her to relax but her muscles won't stop convulsing. She is in a half sit-up position, engaging her core. I try to get her to relax but she keeps looking at me.

"Are you ok?" she asks.

"Of course," I say, but then I realize I'm crying.

"Fuckin' weirdo."

 "No – Jesus – I'm so sorry."

The girl pulls the towel around her again and stands up.

"It's important that we make sure there is nothing in there that shouldn't be," I plead.

"It's ok," the girl says. "I'll try again myself."

"This is very a serious condition. It could be life-threatening. I can't let you go without knowing for sure."

The girl pulls back on her trousers. "I'll be fine," she says. And then she's gone.

I can still remember what Nicole wore to the first Junior Disco in the local GAA hall – a pink halter-neck, a denim skirt that she rolled up so that her bum cheeks peeked out at the bottom and a pair of Adidas runners. We had lost touch at that stage. She was rumored to have kissed thirteen boys that night, one of whom became the first of a long string of boyfriends. She didn't handle break-ups well. It didn't help that every failed relationship sparked new graffiti in the girls' toilets. *Nicole Day sucks dick. Nicole Day is a slut.* After a particularly difficult break-up, she was found dead in her bedroom after hanging herself from her wardrobe. We were thirteen years old.

On my way home I buy a homeless man hot chocolate to make myself feel better. It only occurs to me while standing in the queue getting ready to order on the man's behalf that he might not like hot chocolate. I order one anyway.

"Cream and marshmallows?"

"Yes please."

"What's your name?"

"Emma, but –" It's too late, the marker has already swirled my name on the cup. I consider getting a pen and scribbling *from* in front of Emma but that would bring a whole new level of shame. I am already making the poor man suffer through whipped cream and marshmallows for my own benefit.

I drop the hot chocolate down beside the man's cardboard sign and slip a twenty-euro note into his cup of change as an apology for letting them write my name on the hot chocolate. I don't look at him as I pass.

I'm in bed trying to get some sleep when my phone vibrates under my pillow. I have a new match on Tinder. I click into the notification expecting to see the face of some guy who just about passed the seems-normal-enough test. It's Tom.
I'm embarrassed at how hard my heart is beating. I click into my profile to review the photos of me that he is seeing for the first time. I already know how it's going to go. We'll go for a drink. When we kiss, I will try my best to find the sadness in him and make him feel like everything will be ok. I'll get to see his apartment or I'll bring him back to mine and I'll fall asleep with my head on his chest and his arms wrapped around me. It won't take long for us to figure out that we're not right for each other. We'll be able to keep up the lie for a month or two and there will be another few awkward months of running into each other on the corridors in work. I know how to manage my expectations. I already know how it's going to work out, but I also really, really need a hug.

My phone vibrates again. He's sent a message.

Hi Emma

Hi Tom

How are you?

I'm in dire need of a pint. That last patient was a nightmare.

Oh cool, you're a doctor as well?

He doesn't recognize me. I try to rationalize my reaction. It's fine. He's not well. We're not right for each other anyway. It doesn't matter that he doesn't remember me. I delete the conversation from my phone.

The next morning I get up before the alarm and go to the toilet. I pull out the string of the parcel, holding it up to examine like a dead mouse dangling by its tail. I flush the blood away, wash the memory of the girl off my hands.

PARASITE
Rose Keating

Jessica wasn't sure what to do, and Mother seemed disinclined to help. Mother just sat there looking up at her, right into her eyes. It made Jessica's skin feel tight, too small for her too-warm brain. Jessica was sweating; she could feel the wet slick of it on her forehead and eyelids. She wanted to wipe the sweat away but did not want to do it with her Mother's gaze on her. She did not know what to do with her hands either. She clenched and unclenched them at her sides and repressed the urge to bite at the skin of her cuticles.

'We should probably start at some point,' Mother said. Her eyes remained on Jessica while she spoke, her face unchanging.

Jessica knew Mother wasn't the warmest person, but she didn't know that irises could become ice. That pupils could freeze. Jessica didn't know what she had done to put that ice in her Mother's eyes. She would do anything to take it away.

Jessica leaned towards Mother, closer to her face. She hesitated, conscious of her heavy breathing against Mother's cheek. Mother raised a single eyebrow, and Jessica drew back, embarrassed.

She looked at the stretched skin of neck in front of her. Considered it. Thought of lions and lunging and wide deer eyes and David Attenborough describing the rip of skin and sinew in a calm, cultured voice. Predator and prey. Teeth and tear and torn. Animals. Animals go for the throat. It made her shudder. Hesitantly she reached for her Mother's hand instead and lifted it up.

'We can stop if you can't figure it out,' Mother said. Mocking, but Jessica swore she could hear something else. It felt like an undercurrent of something sad and ugly. Like a plea that didn't know how to enter the world.

Jessica thought of all the girls in the school yard, lips heavy in pout and hips rounding out. Boys' glances lingering now. They were fleshy and solid in a way that she wasn't; they seemed more human. Just a little more here than Jessica. Doll Jessica, waifish and small. Barely there and hardly even real. Pinocchia wanted to be a real girl. Just wanted to be like them; that's all she wanted. That wasn't wrong; why wouldn't Mother want that for her? Jessica needed this. Jessica was owed this.

'I want to do it. I want to do it now,' she said, and brought her Mother's hand to her mouth.

She gripped the hand between her teeth. Her tongue against the thick pad below thumb. It smelled like lotion and lemon washing-up liquid.

Jessica bit.

Skin split. Her Mother leaked. Jessica saw. She saw and saw and saw.

Her Mother bled winter.

Ice. The way air hardens to ice as you choke it down in November. The body choking down air was an Emily. Emily was sixteen. Slim and tall; the thrill of knowing your body is a thing of power. Her beautiful machine, a long-legged joy. She could command armies with it. But instead here at sixteen, her hand in the hand of him. Him, a little shorter than her with big, brown doe eyes. Looking up at her like his bones were about to melt. She wanted to learn to melt. Frozen girl full of ice blood. She breathed frost into her gut as she stood next to this boy of blush and bubble. He was so warm. Made the diamond ice of her guts vibrate and crack. Who knew it would ever feel so good to crack? And so she let him. She let the doe boy lean up and press his lips to hers. Emily let him teach her how to melt.

Jessica broke away.

There was blood on her lip; it tasted like frost. She wiped her lip and swallowed a lodged hunk of flesh that she hadn't quite got down. Her head was ringing. Her brain felt so full, being bursting. There was a thunderstorm exploding in her gut. It hurt so good.

She had ripped this from her. From Mother. This thing. This memory. This ice in the pit of her stomach. It was not hers, it was Mother's. She has stolen it from her Mother and taken it in to her gut.

Her Mother was pale and her eyes were dimmed. She no longer met Jessica's gaze.

'I – are you, I mean, are you okay?' Jessica asked.

Her mother did not respond. Jessica's heart was rabbit-fast battering against her chest. The silence screamed at her. Her eyes stung and her blood throbbed. Her arms ached with the absence of someone to hold on to. She reached out with her throbbing, sweaty arms and tried to put them around her Mother. Her Mother recoiled and stood up. She refused to look at Jessica as she left the room.

Jessica sat in the too-quiet kitchen and let the silence scrape at her insides until she had unlearned what it was to move.

Minutes or centuries later, she heard her phone ping beside her. She broke the cement air and picked it up; a message from the girls. They wanted to know how it went was it good how did it feel did you like it do you want to come over. They were all at Melanie's.

Jessica grabbed her keys and left.

'I just don't understand why she had to be such a bitch about it,' Melanie said. 'I mean, it's her job. She should be grateful, to be honest-'

The girls sat in a semi-circle around Jessica, clad in cotton pyjamas, eyes hungry for details. They all nodded solemnly in agreement at Melanie's words.

Jessica looked at the ground and tugged at a thread at the knee of her pants. She had passed Melanie's mother on the way in. She looked normal, but Jessica knew she was mostly hollow now. Melanie had told them in class that she had started from the inside first. Her father was a surgeon; he had helped. An efficient method, judging by the heavy globes attempting to burst through the buttons of Melanie's shirt.

'I mean, I don't know. I didn't want to upset her,' Jessica said. 'Maybe I shouldn't have done it-'

The others gasped in unison. Outrage ran like a pulse through the group.

Jessica no

Jessica this is her job

Jessica everyone has to do it

Jessica you know you can't avoid it

Jessica she is a mother she knew what that meant from the start

Jessica you need this

Jessica you deserve it

Jessica she's the one who's wrong

Jessica she's jealous she's petty she's selfish she's a bitch she's a cunt Jessica fuck her

Jessica she had her time it's your time now

Jessica a good mother would never do this Jessica a good mother would only want the best for you

Jessica she's a bad mother Jessica you deserve better a good mother would be grateful

Jessica you deserve this

Jessica felt the words run through her, fire hot. Sticking to her skin and sinking into her pores. They slithered their way into her veins and pumped up into her aorta. She was flooded with them and she knew. She knew they were right. Their words lit her brain cells up dragon bright. She would fight. She would take. Because she deserved it. She deserved every last bite.

The air had become tight with anger and felt like it was about to burst. Someone pierced a pin through the pressure by asking if anyone wanted to watch Dirty Dancing. The pressure of the room wheezed out through the pin hole in the form of uncertain chuckles, and a gasp of delight, and a few groans. The groans were eventually shot down, and the disc was roughly shoved into the DVD player by over eager hands.

Melanie padded over to Jessica's spot on the floor and sat down. She wore plush woollen socks that looked a little worn, a toe peeking out through a hole at the top. Jessica kept her eyes glued to the tight pants and toned abs on screen as that toe gently prodded at her own foot. The other girls were deep into a discussion regarding the merits of Patrick Swayze versus John Travolta and did not notice them.

'Jess?' Melanie said. Jessica looked over to her. Melanie's eyes were heavily lidded, looking at Jessica in a slight squint. Her mouth was too round to be a cupid's bow, full little half moons slathered in clear lip gloss. Jessica quickly looked away from it, nodding in response to Melanie's not-question. From the corner of her eye, Jessica could see that mouth quirk into a smile.

'Have you ever been kissed Jess?'

Jessica kept her eyes trained carefully on screen, but her hands involuntarily rose to her mouth. On the television a leather-clad crotch rolled again a pert bottom. She bit ferociously at a hangnail. 'No,' Jessica whispered back, 'Have you?'

Melanie's smile widened as she leaned in towards Jessica. She smelled like talcum powder and floral body spray. She pressed her upper body against Jessica's. Jessica wondered if the globes really would burst through the buttons of her shirt. As she put her mouth towards Jessica's ear, Jessica swore she felt a glob of her lip gloss drip slowly down on to the lobe.

'Yes,' Melanie said, and the wet part of her bottom lip flicked against the skin of Jessica's ear as she said it. Jessica's lungs had forgotten how to breathe.

Melanie drew back, her half-moons melting to a smirk.

'Don't worry,' she said, 'Now that you've started, we'll get one of the guys for you soon.'

Melanie's father drove her home. Told her he was glad to hear that she had finally started the process.
'I know it can be hard at the start. Christ, I left the house whenever Mel began eating. Mel's mother needed to start, so it was for the best. She had gotten old. Don't get me wrong, not like I was trying to rush it on. But nothing's forever, you know? Out with the old, and well, you know how it is,' he chuckled.

Jessica hummed in response and drummed her fingers against her knees, looking anywhere but at him.

'She was a fine woman in her day, Mel's mother. Beautiful, in a proper Hollywood kind of way. Sagging a bit now, so starting was for the best. And Melanie's gotten so damn pretty since she's started. Not quite her mother, but still, sweet little thing. We've gotten real, real close now, since it all started. Can't help but notice. A real looker, you know? Don't worry, you'll fill out too, soon,' he said.

He dragged his gaze slowly up and down her body. He smiled.

The next day, nothing had changed too dramatically in the mirror, but still, lips a little fuller. Cheeks a little less plump, shape finding her bones. Jessica stripped off her clothes piece by piece and looked back to the mirror.

And this, this was why. This was why she had to do it. Legs longer, waist lengthened. Chest sprout. Hair tangle between thighs. Creamy and splattered with red. She must have leaked during the night. Her first one.

She pressed her hand to the leak. Not pure. Dirty and thick and congealed. It smelled sweet in a meaty sort of way. Like butcher shops and over-ripe fruit. Gone-off strawberries. Not pure. Not just blood. It was all the bits of her, leaking out. Jessica lifted her red fingers to her mouth. Coagulated blackberry meat clinging in places. She licked her fingers. The birth of her in her mouth.

Jessica sat down on her bed and thought about Mother. Mother hadn't spoken to her since last night, when Jessica had stolen the memory of what a kiss tastes like from her. Her Mother would never get that back. The memory was in Jessica's stomach now, being broken down by acid and bile. She had bitten into her hand and gulped down skin and snow. But this. This was why it was worth it.

Over the weeks that followed, Jessica took:

A bit of jaw. Her Mother's favourite colour was golden yellow, like honey catching fire.

A piece of shoulder. Her Mother's wedding song had been 'Can't Help Falling in Love', the Elvis version, crooning and sticky and just a bit bitter sweet.

A thumb. Her Mother's first trip abroad by herself. She met a man in Florence who licked ice cream out of her mouth. She was engaged to Jessica's father at the time.

An eyelid. Her Mother had been a dancer when she was young. She had wanted to travel the world with her ensemble. Father stuck a ring on her finger. So she didn't.

A hunk of neck. Her Mother told people that her favourite movie is Gone With the Wind, but Jessica learned that it is not. Her Mother's favourite movie was The Godfather. She watched it whenever she had the house to herself. She gorged herself on every shot and threat and mouthed along to every line. She dreamed about the feel of a gun in her hand. She dreamed about wearing a suit and fucking girls and cocking a weapon and telling some asshole to shut the fuck up.

An ear. Her Mother loved gazpacho.

As autumn greyed into winter, her Mother became littered with holes. Jessica tried to take no more than a bite or two a week. She wanted to make it last as long as possible; no one had told her just how good it would feel. Sometimes Father would place bandages over the wounds, touch cloud wisp light, like he was afraid she would shatter. He spent more and more time away from the house.

The girls in school told Jessica this was normal; their mothers were the same. Normal, at their age. It had to happen eventually. Everyone loses bits and pieces of themselves over the years.

Jessica kept growing. Inches and pounds in days. Gained soft layers to her thighs and hips. The pad of her stomach. Lying on the bed, legs spread. Her body becoming a peach split drip. Chest heavier; she knew she should be wearing a bra by now. Father kept his eyes averted when he was there and was careful not to touch her when he passed her in the hall.

Jessica didn't want the bra. Skin feeling taut and tense and tender. Her body the moment before a scream, or a moan. She wanted to stretch and twist and feel the weight of all this new meat in the world.

Jessica had grown softer, more rounded than Mother had been. Mother always elegant angles and endless leg. But Mother, never this. Not skin shrinking into bone and bone shrinking into hollow. Her body trying to disappear into Jessica's new inches. Jessica's friends said it was the same for them. Their mothers shrinking and full of holes. Mothers keep on going even as their wounds drip out all over the kitchen floors. The fathers turn their gaze elsewhere.

Mother was softening also, in a different sense. Her resentment was quieting. Some hard part of her was breaking, or withering. She did not glare when Jessica lifted her parts to her mouth. Jessica did not know why. Maybe she was finally accepting this, and happy for Jessica. Happy to give Jessica this part of herself.

Sometimes Jessica wondered if maybe she had just eaten the part of her Mother that knew how to fight back.

More and more of the memories Jessica took were about dancing. Stage, lights, feet cramps. Sometimes just sounds and images; Bach like toffee thread light in the parlour and red wine smoke of Chopin rising through the house in wisps.

Father's favourite singer was Randy Travis. Jessica could hear it playing from upstairs when she came home from school on Friday evening.

Her Mother looked peaceful. She smiled, softly, when Jessica met her eyes. She rolled her eyes at Randy Travis. Her mother was an Emily was her Mother was a human. Jessica was beginning to understand. They were all there in her at once. Mother sat there that night and Emily glinted in her eyes.
Mother looked at Jessica for a long time, before finally stretching her neck to the side.

Jessica gaped. An offering. Freely given. This is my body, this is my blood. Given up for you. For me, thought Jessica, all for me.

Jessica leaned in. Jessica bit.

A room filled with people, music; a party. Doe eyed boy was there, sneaking glances at her from the kitchen door. She walked over to him and took his hand and led him to a closet. She kissed lips and neck and groin and took off her clothes and guided his hands and then the grind slap in and out she was alive she was alive squeal wheel until. Until explosion shatter, body becoming a rainbow ripple, a hole spewing up colour and him there with her too. They held each other through it, waiting for the spasms to stop. Doe eyed boy trailed his fingers up and down her arm and looked up at her with eyes soft enough to bruise.

Emily went home, and watched her stomach grow bigger. She wore baggy jumpers to cover up until she couldn't cover it anymore. She went to doe eyed boy to show him what had happened.

Emily expected shock. Maybe horror, maybe stuttering or shouting or tears. She did not expect the slow, wide smile that spread across his face. She did not expect him to sink to his knees and press his hands to her stomach. She did not expect him to lift up her jumper and press a soft kiss to the spot just below her belly button.

She shoved him away, hard. He fell backwards. He looked up at her from where he lay sprawled.

'Emily, will you marry me?' he asked.

'I don't want to marry you,' she replied, and saw the hurt on his face, 'I don't want to marry anyone.'

'But we're going to have a baby, we have to get married,' he said.

'I don't want a baby,' she said.

'Well, it's too late for that. Not like you can stop it. You know that. Don't really get a choice in that now,' he said.

'I don't love you,' she said.

Doe boy got to his feet. Emily stepped backwards, away from him. He followed and backed her against the wall. He lifted his hand to her face and trailed his thumb against her cheek.

'You will, someday,' he said, and leaned in and kissed her.

Jessica's Mother pushed her away.

Jessica ignored her. She was reeling, stomach twisting painfully. Vinegar hitting the back of her throat. She closed her eyes from crowded party overfull and music so loud and her Father who used to be a doe smiling from across a room.

Jessica lunged to her Mother's neck and bit and tore and swallowed and did not stop. Throat. Tongue. Chest. Breast. Stomach. Gut. Womb.

Jessica's Mother didn't do much of anything, after that. Couch for hours. Sometimes the bed instead. She watched a lot of EastEnders after that night. Just like the other girls' mothers. Melanie's mother was a fan of Fair City.
She didn't speak a lot, either. Just sat, hours and hours of sitting. Silence. So heavy. No

Bach. No Randy Travis, even. Father had left a little while after he saw what happened. Couldn't stand to see her walking around riddled with so many holes, pretending like it was all alright. Just her and Mother then.

Jessica wanted to believe that they didn't need him. She wanted to believe that she could be enough for her and Mother. She didn't need him; she could be enough for the both of them. Then she would spot Mother's tiny body lying on her too big bed. Jessica wasn't even sure how much of him her Mother remembered. How much of doe eyed boy had been taken from her. One side of the bed never, ever slept on. Enough of her body parts remembered his touch to make a shrine of rumpled bed sheets. At times like that Jessica broke a little. At times like that Jessica understood the difference between want and need.

Jessica had taken to sitting with her, because she didn't know what else to do. Crying wouldn't make it better. She didn't deserve to cry. Parasite. Jessica was a parasite. She had finally realised it. No tits or cunt blood could make up for that. Every bit of her being was stolen. Taint. There was dirt in her blood.

Mother still maintained muscle movement. She would, right up until Jessica had eaten the muscle. Dying is too easy an option for mothers. They do not get that option. Their nerve endings will continue to wriggle down to the very last strand until digested. Consumption is the only way out for them. Mother had taken to smiling at Jessica and offering her wrist to her whenever she passed. Jessica slapped it away and ran to the toilet, vomiting over and over until only stomach acid came up.

She left the house that night, vomit on her chin and clinging to her hair. Her friends from school were having a party. It'll be fun, they said. New year, new you, they said.

Jessica went and she drank. She drank and drank and drank and it hurt her throat and the pain did not make her feel alive. It just made her blur. Gas over her eye balls. Her brain dissolving into mist and nausea. Her limbs had forgotten where her muscles were. Movement impossible. A body smashing their mouth in to hers.

That body led her to a closet. A boy. A stranger. Slumped over, her body soggy sag. She did not have to guide him. But no alive, no alive. No colour blinding orchestral climax. Jessica barely there. And then spill spill uh oh anyway. He zipped up. Left immediately after. Jessica sat in the dark. She eventually picked herself up and opened the door.

'You look so good, Jess,' Melanie said to her when she passed her in the kitchen. Jessica looked down at her body.

She saw the fingers that Emily had used to tie her ballet shoes before going on stage. She saw the stomach that had grown and bulged and split with tiger stripes as Jessica grew in Emily's womb. She saw feet that had stepped on doe boy's toes by accident the first time he had asked Emily to dance. She saw breasts that had grown and sagged with milk, cracked and bleeding and sore when Emily had fed Jessica. She saw Emily's arm that had broken when she had fallen from a tree she had climbed to prove a point to her boy. She saw the hands that had placed her ballet shoes into the bin in her garden with gentle care the evening after doe eyed boy proposed to her.

Jessica looked up from her stolen costume and smiled at Melanie.

'Thank you, Melanie,' she said, and did not scream. She continued to smile and not scream as she walked all the way out of the house and back to her home and into her kitchen.

Things can be stolen. Jessica knew this. Things could also be returned.

Jessica took a knife out of the drawer and walked into the living room. Her Mother sat on the couch in the dark, also smiling and not screaming. Jessica turned on the light.

She looked at her Mother. She looked at that tiny body littered with holes. She looked into her eyes. Her Mother was so beautiful.

She put her arms around her Mother. Her Mother smiled dumbly and put her arms around Jessica in reciprocation. Jessica could feel the open wounds of Mother's arms seeping on to her dress. Jessica gently pushed her away after a moment.

She took the knife and cut a hunk of her wrist off without hesitation. It hurt, but it hurt so good. She could give it back. She could give it all back. She took the hunk and yanked her Mother's jaw open and shoved it down her throat.

'I love you,' Jessica said.

Smoke
Valerie Lutte

My heart is a black hole

     We are just two girls kissing on my mother's front porch. It's strange since I only moved back here recently and my parents don't know I also date girls. We are so still that as we kiss, the motion light above us turns off. I unlock the front door then tell her to wait for me.

"Will I have time for a smoke?" she asks, fingering the pack in the front pocket of her jeans.

Inside, waiting for sleep

     Rachel sits in front of the television. It's playing something about the destruction of the Amazon rainforest, but she isn't paying attention. It's late. She doesn't know how late. After a certain hour, her eyes can't adjust to read the tiny numbers on the cable box clock. From the foyer, she can hear the sound of the front door unlocking. She remembers the days when her daughter came home from school in the afternoons and she would always try to be near the door when it opened. It's too late for her to move now.

I hear the television

     I poke my head into the living room. Sometimes the pain keeps my mother from sleeping. Still, it's late for her, being almost three. On the couch, she looks carved from granite—gray and rigid.

     Her eyes roll towards me. "Kitty, you're home." The slur of Percocet is in her voice.

     "Feeling alright?" I say.

     "No, no. I kept tossing and turning. It felt like fire in my legs. Finally, I came down here."

     She's too honest sometimes.

Thrown in darkness

     Rachel shuts off the TV, the only light in the room, and then asks her daughter for a hand. She slips her arm in Rachel's and walks with her. Her daughter's arms are cold and thin—too thin, it seems, for a 22 year old. Rachel can feel the bone, soft and bendable as a wishbone. It feels wrong for her to lean on it.

We blink in brightness

I turn on the hall lights before we tackle the stairs. The wall of the staircase is lined with pictures of my brother and me from infancy to the recent past. As my mother and I climb, the round baby faces turn into skinny children, then sullen teenagers. My mother's body feels heavy. The opiates have left her half-asleep, half-aware.

My last photo, at the top of the stairs, is my college graduation. My brother's is his wedding. Even though he's only three years older than me, he managed to get into the world before the recession. He got a job before his last semester of college ended, got married a month later, and bought a house on the other side of the state.

I am here. I am helping my mother up the stairs.

A girlfriend waits outside.

Carrying home smoke

From the bar, the scent of cigarettes is soaked into her daughter's clothes and hair. Rachel had quit smoking years ago, when the kids were in grade school, but she could go for one on a night like tonight—a summer night when time itself, as if slippery with humidity, seems to slide backwards.

She waits for me

Outside, the girl's probably leaning against the railing. On a hot night like this, the white vinyl might cool her forearms where she rests them. She'd swat at a mosquito attracted by the stagnant water in the flower pots on either side of the door. Maybe she would slip her sockless feet out of her stuffy combat boots and slide her toes against the cement. But she'd put her shoes back on to crush her cigarette butt, which she'd politely pocket before she lights up again.

The end of the hall is still black

Rachel had moved into her son's old room on the far side of the hall. She doesn't like to wake her husband when she gets up in the middle of the night. She'll jerk up and have to stretch one leg and then the other until the numbness stops.

The sheets will be cold when she gets in.

I bring the girl inside

Except she's not really a girl. "I'm beyond gender," she tells me. "I don't get trapped in categories." I kiss her again.

I'm within gender. I'm trapped in everything.

My secret

My mother doesn't know I also date girls, not because I think she'd mind, but because everything seems too personal to talk about: what song I'd been listening to on repeat (*The Descendents* – 'Suburban Home'), what television show I watched at 5 AM yesterday (*Twilight Zone with Rod Serling*). I need to keep everything inside me. Otherwise there won't be anything left.

Someone is inside

Rachel can hear the voices as she is lying down. She knows her daughter brought someone home, brought someone home and didn't want her to know. She's an adult now, Rachel reminds herself. But she is still so small.

The girl in my room

I knew her before, before she was beyond gender. We were friends in high school, then we talked less and less. She stayed in town after graduation. I didn't expect her to change.

We called her Maricela back then, before she was beyond gender. Now she goes by Marc or Marcy or Weevil or Martinez.

The pain is worse in bed

The pain. At this point, Rachel is afraid to go to sleep if it means she will oversleep tomorrow. The doctors are supposed to call early. If she's not up, her husband won't know what questions to ask, her daughter won't. There is no one she can lean on for this.

As Mick Jagger once said

Please allow me to introduce myself: I've been called Kitty or Kitty Weiss or just Weiss. I've been called stupid goth and I've been called nerd. I've been called femme and I've been called dyke. I've been called whore and I've been called frigid bitch. I've called myself dirty and I've been called destructive. I've been called Kit, but never Kit Weiss.

Time slides backwards

Back to when her little girl was small enough to lift. Rachel would pick her up from under the arms, and Kitty would laugh and swing her dangled feet. Her feet were soft and perfect and white. What kind of information did those nerves transfer that led to such happiness—how did they recognize the cool air, the freedom. The blissful, healthy nerves of someone so young. And in Rachel's own feet, she felt nothing more than the eternal firmness of the earth supporting her.

We sleep huddled like animals

But I must have only slept a couple hours, because it is still dark outside. I can just barely make out the black square of the shirtless Sid Vicious poster I put on my ceiling back in ninth grade. One corner is peeling off—the one noticeable change since high school. Same pink carpet with nail polish stains (black), the same furniture covered in nicks and band stickers. And I thought I had gone to college for wisdom.

I look at her, still sleeping

The girl's arm, curled over her stomach is covered in downy hairs, like a baby's. Her breasts are just as small and hard as they were in high school, underdeveloped, the body of someone not yet fully a woman. And yet, she tells me she knows who she is.

By 5 AM

Rachel has given up on sleep. She goes downstairs to make a pot of coffee. First she changes the filter, filling the room with the bitter smell of still moist grounds. The glass sliding doors in the kitchen reveal the blue-grey sky that proceeds the black hour before dawn.

I remember

Once my mother spoke at a rally in the state capital building. I was maybe ten years old. Protestors from all over the state had already crowded under the fresco dome. They lined the balconies, holding their hand-painted posters over the edge. My mother's hand found mine. Her large, soft hands smelled like menthol—she still smoked then.

I stood awkwardly at the foot of the staircase as she walked up the first steps. She turned back to me, and her grinning eyes met mine as she spoke.

"Politicians are trying to dirty our state. They think its beauty belongs to them and their corporate buddies. It doesn't. It belongs to all of us, and more importantly, to our children."

A whoop rang out from the back of the room.

"It is up to us to protect it."

Louder cheers this time as her words grew more forceful. I had never seen this side of her before—she seemed as solid and stable as the white marble she stood on.

She continued, "To protect it not just for ourselves, but for our children, like my daughter here." She pointed. I could feel the eyes as she stepped down and applause filled the room. At that moment, I felt like my mom was a superhero, and that through my connection to her, her strength had become my strength.

Begging the question

What makes me think of this now? Was I trying to relive that moment last night? Using my tongue to achieve that ultimate transfer of female power since all other sources have long since gone dry?

The girl's silent breaths seem to heave as she sleeps. It's like she is running a race. The smile on her face says she is winning.

Spoon in the mug

Rachel takes her coffee to the back porch. The air is cool but still weighted by the humidity of summer. The smell of wet earth rises from the yard. She steps into the grass. The ground feels spongy and uncertain.

The girl shifts in her sleep

An open pack of cigarettes lays open on my night stand, spilling in my direction. My last smoke was over four years ago, before I started college, but the nicotine I tasted on the girl last night is singing in my blood. I reach out, ready and willing to submit to any old weakness.

At a loss

Rachel can't remember what she watched the night before. She can remember her daughter walking through the fog. Kitty's pale skin seemed to glow in the blue light of the television, a glow she carried around the room like the cold presence of a ghost.
But what words were exchanged? She can see Kitty's jaw working up and down, but the sound is gone. Her eyes had a sense of urgency. What if her words had cracked the walls between them and Rachel couldn't remember? She trusted it hadn't. If in doubt, assume all things remain the same.

All I know

My last cigarette was during a time in my life when I felt like had future and opportunity—I mean really believed it, not repeated it in my mind like I do now. I felt like I had the power to end any bad habit. But I can't remember the specifics, a conscious moment of quitting.

The air in my bedroom is so stuffy, like it and time are standing still. I get up to open the window and step on my black nail polish stain. If I could walk back in time, like I can walk across my memories stained on this carpet, could I make events any way I want them to be?

Kicking off her slippers

Rachel feels slick grass beneath her feet. She curls her toes into the soft dirt as she finishes her coffee. She sets her mug down, but it falls over on the uneven ground. She doesn't see the last few drops disappear into the grass. Unburdened, she spins. It's been years since she's done this—been barefoot in her yard. Dew moves up her ankles. Time slides off her. The sky is getting darker, as it does just before dawn.

Lighting up

My last smoke could have been the night and Maricela went to the playground to behind my old elementary school, the summer before I left for college. (We called her Maricela back then. Back before she was beyond gender.) It must have been nearly midnight but the air was still hot and sticky as dog's breath. We shared her pack of Luckies.

"So Kit, old college-gal," she said. She always called me Kit. Other people called me Kitty or Kitty Weiss or even K-rad. "How soon do you think it'll be before you never speak to me again?" We were on the bridge part of the jungle gym so any move either one of us made rocked us both. She leaned back, propped up on her elbows. It felt weird talking to her because I couldn't see her face. I could only see the red glow of her cigarette as she reached over to drop ashes off the railing.

"What are you talking about?" The air tasted sour from the diesel smell that drifted from the nearby highway. I sucked down my cigarette to drown it out.

"Kit, Kit, I'm sure we'll mean well. It won't be right away. I mean, you're leaving this wasteland to be an environmental engineer or some superhero shit." She pushed herself up just far enough so I could see her eyes, though just barely in the darkness. "I don't expect your high school smoke buddy to fit into that."

Her head had dropped beyond view again. The only sound was the endless drone of cars on the highway. There'd be nothing but aimless wanderers out at this time of night.

"If you're going to pull this petty high school shit, you won't be hearing from me. Count on that." I grabbed her Luckies and threw them at her, targeting where I thought her face would be. I missed, but my sudden motion shook us both.

I dropped my cigarette butt over the bridge, and it disappeared among the grey strips of tanbark.

An escape

I blow smoke through the window screen. The sky is black outside my bedroom window, but the outline of trees looming at the end of the backyard is still visible. I close my eyes, focus on drawing the poison into my lungs. I hold my breath before each exhale. I don't choke. I don't cough. It feels as warm and familiar as a favorite blanket.

She spins still

The smoke drifts to Rachel, like a dream that comes at the end of a fitful night's sleep. She feels the pain in her feet, shooting up her legs, but she keeps spinning. Her eyes well with tears, but she keeps spinning.

My eyes open

My mother dances in the yard, her white nightgown billowing around her legs. From here she looks small and delicate, like a little girl. Her arms stretch out, as if in reverence, as she twirls. The sky is turning towards light. I watch her through the smoke. She might never stop.

MOTHER
Mercedes Lawry

Wind rummages the regiments of tall grass,
a hiss across the valley. Inside
a small white house, a dying woman.

Her daughter casts spells as long days empty
to darkness, star-speckle, false hope.
A rosary winks from a bedpost.

All of the liars have passed by the house —
sun, rain, bitter moons, blooms
of vast assortment, endless colour.

Breath slows and almost disappears
The daughter has entered a shell
of her own making. No light gets in.

The mother is here and not here,
the process of departure, witnessed
and denied, embraced and disputed.

Eyes fasten on a window. Outside,
a sugar pine, a wheelbarrow, an old red chair.
The dogs are sleeping in the kitchen.

The daughter rations her movements:
hand on arm, hand smoothing hair, caress,
caress, as if these were enough.

RIGHTEOUS BLOOD
Breda Spaight

In the last year of occasional spotting,
the sudden sight of blood brings me back
to my first; white knickers blood-soaked
as a bullet wound in a cowboy's shirt: a hero's
blood or baddy's — either way, blood was male.

Before television, blood is the figure of Christ
on the cross — my original almost-naked man.
His ribs like handlebar finger grips;
the hollow between biceps and triceps curved
like a lip on his sallow stretched arms;

long muscles of the stomach tautened,
rippled as a beach at low tide;
his body pierced with bleeding slits —
the holy wounds of palms and feet,
and the flow from his divine gash.

It was still a time of sin, and I believed
I'd burn for recognising Christ's nipples
on David Bowie. The profanity of Ziggy's body —
pale lean legs, slender arch of the cheekbones
rouged: a man who could menstruate;

the hallowed male now liberated
from the cross to bleed among women;
know the curse of monthly mouthfuls spewed
to the summons of the moon — never noble,
never sacred.

GOOD GIRLS DON'T BLEED
P.C. Vandall

(For Kiran Gandhi who ran the London Marathon without a tampon)

Shame on you for not being more discreet,
and sanitary, for not dressing it up
as Aunt Flow, Cousin Ruby and Uncle
Tom. You must've known there would be fall out,

that papers would spatter your blood-soaked tights
for the whole world to see. This is not
The Sisterhood of the Travelling Pants!
What made you think you could go with the flow?

Women have spent years covering it up,
veiling it in darkness and pretending
it doesn't exist. Who bloody cares
that you trained for a year? Who gave you

the right to run by the seat of your soiled
red pants? I've been to the segregated
classrooms, seen sculpted-pink interlocking
parts pulled from plastic nesting vaginas.

I have felt the humiliation
of my discharge from the uterine
army. You leaked out our secret and now
we'll be on the run forever. They may

confine us to huts, burn us at the stake
and call us Eve-ill. I watched you cross
the finish line, your bright face shining
like a full moon, your pants singing my shame.

BLUE IN GREEN
Kit de Waal

The second time The Irishman got cancer, someone at the clinic told him there was a painting class for patients. Art therapy they called it. No experience necessary, no talent required, fifteen dollars for a whole afternoon, five off with his Seniors Discount. Would he like to go they said and because he wasn't quick enough with an excuse he found himself signed up. He had no intention of going. But the next day, somehow found him peering through the wired glass door of a small room at the community centre. Before he knew it, he was sitting on a three-legged stool in front of an easel with three or four others in varying stages of disease and acceptance.

The hand on his shoulder told him to paint whatever he felt. When he couldn't work out what he felt, it suggested he paint what he remembered. What he remembered would always start with the colour blue.

So he dipped his brush and covered the sheet of smooth white paper. As he sat and stared at the blue he found himself like a sightseer wandering down the streets and lanes of his childhood finding landmarks. A sunny day, a golden journey to a white sand beach where he made paste from the sand and built a castle with a moat that he filled with silver sparkling sea. He dipped in the yellow. Then he saw himself lying on a carpet of grass under the trees and a thousand dancing leaves. He dipped in the green. Then he was a young man with smooth sun-dyed skin. The brown. And later still, there he was with a bunch of keys, laughing with her. He dipped again into the yellow of her hair and then pure white for the baby he left behind.

But by then The Irishman could no longer see his painting nor the colours on the palette because he had retreated to that time and that place and it was so close that he got up carefully and walked away, back down the corridor and into the canteen.

Now that he knew he was dying some decisions were much easier to make. He was released from denial. Full fat milk, mayonnaise on the ham and cheese, a midday brandy, a cigarette, a fat cigar. He could have anything he wanted and, finding he could at last have them all, freed him completely from desire. Then he got the phone call and everything changed.

The next day The Irishman went to his doctor and got some extra medication for the journey. Then he paid his lawyer seven hundred dollars for an expedited power of attorney. He shoved the envelope into his pocket and stood waiting for the lights to change at Varrick and 22nd Street on his way to see Robbie. Something wasn't right. He must have taken a wrong turn or something. Before he could get his bearings he was told to 'Walk' and the crowd drove him on to the opposite pavement and in front of Robbie's Place except Robbie's Place wasn't there. He took off his sunglasses as though they were shielding the truth but a huge white awning told him he was standing in front of 'Kitchener's. White wood tables, yards of glass and inside green aprons swarmed around with menus and cutlery.

The Irishman took his trilby off and scratched his head shocked to find that he scratched the skin these days. He walked to the corner of the road and checked the street sign. Yes, Robbie's should be there. He replaced his shades and hat and shoved both hands into his tweed overcoat. He had begun muttering in his old age like his father, like old men who have no-one to talk to at home.

'Jesus, where am I?'

He would retrace his steps or walk west towards his old apartment and take it from there. Yes, go west and ask if anyone knew what had happened to Robbie but he had only walked a few hundred yards when it happened again. He turned a corner and where he expected the road with the bus station, he found himself ten feet down a narrow alley between high brick walls.

'God' he said and turned around to make his way back to some sort of familiar territory, worried now, disorientated, uneasy. Christ Almighty, he was lost.

He suddenly became aware, like a cold wind on his back, that someone was behind him. He didn't turn.

'Don't you fucking move!'

In his back The Irishman felt something sharp and hard. It was a knife, not a gun.

'Back up, motherfucker! Quick.'

He shuffled backwards down the alley in the shadow of the buildings, past an old truck where the knife turned him around. The youth he expected was thirty at least, slick with sweat. His electric blue hair stood up inch long on a brick-shaped head, his mouth red and wide. It was dark down the alley and they were hidden by the truck. No one would see them, no one would come. The knife moved from hand to hand.

'You got a watch, take it off, motherfucker! Give me the fucking money, old man. Give me your phone! Now!'

The knife was loose and wild, up in the man's face, down by his groin, his stomach, his shoulder and all the time the instructions and the threats.

'Take off them fucking shades. They're good shades, old guy!'

'Don't make any bad moves, motherfucker or you're going to eat shit.'

'You make any moves, man and you're gonna die!'

'Dead already' The Irishman said as he withdrew his hand from his pocket slowly as though to take his money out. A feint. A slight. A flick from the wrist.

The blue hair scraped along the wall as The Irishman snatched the knife and gave it back to the robber once in the neck and again in the chest where it drove him down on to the concrete. He stood over the body watching the growing blanket of blood.

'Not today, my friend,' he said.

He emerged back onto the busy road in a moment, anyone watching, he thought, would have assumed he had gone down there to relieve himself.

'I'm an old man,' he muttered wiping his hand against his coat, 'I needed a piss.'

And suddenly, at the intersection there it was, Robbie's Place the same sign, the front door, the frieze on the windows.

But inside was entirely different, everything was new and the lights were too bright. Had it not been for Robbie himself leaning on the counter reading a newspaper, The Irishman would have walked out certain that the cancer that was devouring his liver had spread to the part of his brain where he kept his maps, his memories, his sanity.

'Robbie?'

Robbie looked up.

'You found me! They made me an offer on the corner and I had to move the whole enterprise back here. Been here two years, goddamn it! If you came more often... but hey, I got some in the bank and I got me a boat. Come here!'

They embraced like brothers then Robbie slid the glasses from The Irishman's face.

'You don't look so good, buddy? It's come back?'

The man nodded and eased himself on to a bar stool, placing the brown envelope on the counter. Robbie banged down a squat bottle of bourbon and poured two shots.

'Then here's to it. May the grass grow long on the road to hell.'

The Irishman had things to say, something about thanks and friendship but Robbie was watching so he just slid the envelope across the bar.

'I gotta go home.'

Robbie lowered his glass, his drink untouched. The Irishman threw his to the back of his neck.

'Give me a year at most. Then it's yours. Everything.'

At the door he put the shades over his watery eyes and coughed.

'Thank you' he said.

He would have to go quickly now. No one saw him kill the blue dog in the alley but there was no point in wasting time he didn't have. He walked to 22nd street and took a cab home.

In his apartment he opened his suitcase and filled it with the clothes that still fitted him. Then he went to the living room and from a drawer by an old-fashioned record player he took out a pack of cigarettes, a brass lighter and some photographs. He poured himself a cognac and drew the curtains.

The song he wanted to hear was just one cigarette long. There were no words. The Irishman didn't listen to it very often, maybe once every five years. As it played, he shuffled the photographs like a pack of cards, one behind the other.

'I won't need these where I'm going' he said.

But when he went to leave, he wondered should he take the pictures with him just in case.

'In case what?' he muttered. 'I don't want them. I want the real thing.'

He closed the door and hoped that when Robbie opened it in less than a year the smell of the cigarette would be long gone.

MIDDATUN TOWN: THE ROAD'S DREAM

Danny Denton

after the song, Nottamun Town

What happened was—

/

Not a soul would look above or beneath them. Not a soul would. So fixed were they upon—

/

This happened—

/

I worked as a journalist. I was driving out to cover the Midleton parade, anticipating a hundred or so tractors, some Irish dancing, the local karate club doing high kicks down Main Street, the dance club blaring music and gyrating from the flatbed of a delivery truck, many happy old people... I would take ten or so photos, take names, a couple of quotes, make a list and I'd be out the gap inside of two hours—

/

I pulled the car into the hard shoulder to make a phone call. Though I no longer remember who I was calling, I do remember wondering had it ever been so hot on a March day. The Patrick's Days I'd known were usually bright, sure, but windy and cold too. The windscreen intensified the road's heat on my chest and face; while I waited for the call to connect I rolled up my shirt sleeves and took in through the open window the smell of cut grass, the buzzing of things in the fields, and I turned then as a car slowed and stopped alongside me.

Middatun Town? this woman called from her driver's seat. I only remember that she was fair, and the car, a Volkswagen, was grey with a single green stripe running up the bonnet and over the roof. Stopped in the middle of the dual carriageway like that, it was an accident waiting to happen.

Midleton? I corrected her. Next exit, about five kilometres.

No, she said. *Middatun Town.*

Midleton? I stressed.

MID-DA-TUN TOW-EN.

She seemed impatient. Curls of hair stuck to her forehead and she looked not at me when she spoke, but beyond me, to the ditch and fields at my back.

I shrugged, but then suddenly worried that it might be a speech impediment she had.

Midleton, I called, is the next exit, about five kilometres on.

THANKS, she shouted, and she eased the Volkswagen into motion again.

Whoever I was ringing, there was no reception anyway. Even though the reception bars on the mobile were full. It occurred to me then—out of nowhere—that perhaps there was too much reception. And then I saw—

/

Her car, progressing slowly away from me. It was not grey-green now, but black, a sleek vehicle. The road had been deserted (though it was normally a busy road); I couldn't see how it could be any other car, but neither could I see my mistake. Had I hallucinated in the heat? Behind the wheel of my own car, I found myself tearing up the road after her.

Closing in on the vehicle, I could only see that black estate, moving slowly. Compelled to overtake it, I needed to see was the fair-haired woman driving still, to see was the whole thing a trick of the mind, or of the light. I gained and steadily gained. Kept my eyes on the vehicle. I was nearly up with her. Though it was sunny I peered through my windshield as though through a torrential downpour. Pulling into the fast lane and coming up on the black estate's right, I strained to see that driver, and suddenly then found that the ditch was flying at me through my own driver's window, and everything went topsy-turvy—

/

And came to on my side in a dry field, though I am not sure I'd been knocked out.

My shirt was bruised with dirt. A magpie was perched atop a collapsed haybale (it was no time of year for a haybale), pruning her wings and looking at my battered car as a shiny thing she might steal.

I kept pressing at different parts of my body, to be sure I was okay. My thoughts were a bit scrambled, and a voice in my head kept asking me would I be in time for the parade. I need a tractor, I thought, trying hard to focus, to pull the car out of the field. But I knew that all the farmers would be riding tractor in the parade. So anyway, off I went, looking in the upturned wreckage for my phone, which, when I found it, was full of reception bars, yet still no network—

/

My ten toes and the soles of my feet took me the rest of the way to Midleton. Not a car nor soul nor single citizen did I see as I came down off the bypass, only traffic lights and traffic islands. Pavements both smooth and cracked. Infrastructure was the fingerprint and skeleton of many towns now, and as I went, stumbling along—in over the footbridge and down the pavement past the garage, through the little roundabout at the crossroads outside the hotel, onto the big roundabout that had five exits and two lanes and a large wooden boat full of flowers moored on its greengrassy heart—I reflected upon the fact that it was those things that felt real, the roundabouts and roads and traffic islands, and not the town itself. Any town has a rich and full history—of course it does—but I was a journalist. I documented what I saw—

/

Coming down by the TESCO I saw a number of shoppers through the windows, moving up and down the aisles reading shopping lists from A4 pages. I tried to go in to ask about help, for my car and for my aching self, but the automatic doors wouldn't open.

Yoo-hoo! I called, waving in through the glass with no luck.

I realised something odd about the place then. No-one was paying and no-one was running the tills. These people just moved up and down the aisles. They must have been shadow-shoppers, filling baskets for internet orders. Either way, not a soul of them seemed to see me, or to look beneath or above the white sheets of paper in their—

/

I made my way across the empty car park and across the big roundabout in the direction of the town—

/

Midleton. Middatun Town. The main population source of the East Cork County District Region. A single street lined by small, local businesses. A provincial Georgian line on a map. Thirty thousand residents or thereabouts. No building ever made it to the fourth storey. The place with the highest suicide rate in Europe. Four secondary schools (one Gaeltacht), eleven pubs, one proud politician's office: all bypassed west to east by the N25. All hidden beyond the hard shoulder, the fringe of grass, the hoarding...

The river curved in a C at the top and bottom ends of the town; the river held the town in its arc. I had seen a teddy bear floating in it, the previous year, and a gasping dad pulling the teddy up onto the bank, and had heard somewhere the screaming, traumatised child who'd lost the teddy. I'd counted fifty-three tractors in that year's parade, and one float that was simply a bouncy castle tied down onto a trailer. A sign flapped on the trailer; it said PARKINSON REAL ESTATE. I wrote all that down—

/

The first establishment on Main Street—a pub—was packed, it being Paddy's Day, though I'd no trouble getting to the bar.

I crashed my car on the outskirts of town, I said to the bartender, a short brown-haired woman. Just before the slip road. I am not feeling right.

Have a beer, she said. To warm you up. We'll soon get help.

I'll have a tea, I said. It might not be safe to drink if I'm concussed.

Suit yourself, she said.

A girl nursing a pint at my right shoulder said to me, You slipped up before the slip.

I asked her if she knew anyone with a tractor and she laughed.

There was a hustle and a bustle to the place—people of all ages and fashions— and yet there seemed no joy, no camaraderie to the crowd. Wasn't it supposed to be a day of pride and celebration?

I asked the man on my left: Do you know anyone with a tractor? I'm after making a mess of my car on the N25.

He had his eyes fixed on the distance, and seemed like the most sober man in the place.

Are you alright? I asked him.

I couldn't be prouder, he said. My wife gave birth this morning.

Congratulations, I said, striking his shoulder, some physical connection seeming appropriate. Girl or boy?

The most beautiful document you ever did see. He sighed, joyfully. 8.8 megabytes in size. A carbon copy of her grandmother!

8.8 megabytes? I asked.

Does anyone here own a tractor? I asked, in vain. Has anyone seen a guard? I've no mobile reception. Is there anyone here that speaks any fucking sense?

The place was full and yet I was alone. Feeling suddenly, overwhelmingly drunk, I caught the barmaid's eye.

I better have that pint after all, I said. I need to sober up.

She gave me that look that all barmaids and barmen have in their arsenal, the look that says, rightfully, that they knew better than you all along—

/

The pub was a long wood-panelled corridor. Mirrors ran along behind the till and the spirit shelves, and the spirits reflected in the cloudy mirrorglass so that it seemed there were twice as many bottles, and tills, and punters, seen from both in front and behind. Or, put another way, when I looked at the people and the spirits and the tills themselves, it seemed that there were half as many.

I overheard a woman and a man talking about a tattoo she had on her hard white bicep. It depicted a creature's head, a ghoulish hairless thing with four oblong eyes, one stacked upon the other, and a wide grinning mouth of rounded baby's teeth.

I seen that thing before, the man said to her, admiring it with folded arms.

Where'd you see it before? she asked.

In my dream, he replied.

I got it when he was six months old, she said.

And there was another individual, who looked extraordinarily like my own mother, seated in a tiny chair at the very back of the pub, right by the front door. Her chair and back were to the wall, like she was an animal making sure it couldn't be ambushed, trying to make herself as small as possible in that chair, or the mirrorcloudy room as big as possible, and when I ventured as far as I could that way I heard her to say... Something, I can't remember exactly now. And it wasn't a woman at all, but an old man—

/

I was still searching the pub for a farmer or a guard when word filtered through that the parade was imminent.

The citizens finished their pints and pulled on their coats and hats, and it was all come ons and seeyelaters, and I swear I heard pigeon wings beating the air, or computer hard-drives flithering.

In dribs and drabs, but as one crowd, we pressed out into the one Middatun Main Street to see the parade. All our umbrellas—every colour of the rainbow, but mostly green or black—went straight up, though the sun was still belting down its cold, soaking rays. The kids all had these green-white-gold hairbands, and jester hats, and top hats, and flags, and cakes, and facepaint. The adults had lots of the same, but they also had cigarettes and mobile phones and take-away coffee cups and car keys, and other things that were darker and harder to understand. There was anticipation and gossip and laughter and giddiness in all the sounds of the parade crowd, but when I looked in their eyes... Their eyes looked neither up nor down the street in anticipation of the parade, but straight out to the patch of empty road in front of them. And for a split second I thought of that town as gone forever, only a memory.

But then I was looking up and down the street, and I saw an open lorry trailer, parked on the pavement up the way, with a row of six or seven school chairs on it, in a line, giving a great view of the length of the street. It was where the dignitaries sat and watched the parade, where the speeches would be made.

Who are those two? I asked a tall woman eating candy floss beside me. I pointed at the overcoated boy and girl seated in the middle seats on the trailer.

That's the Grandmother and Grandfather of the town, she said. Guests of honour each year.

Are they not a bit young?

She looked in my direction like I was mad.

Where am I? I begged her.

Middatun Town, she said, and I wondered if she was the woman from the green-grey-black Volkswagen. Or the estate. Or whatever. Memory, ha!

Then a single drum rang out.

That crowd were louder than ever but I heard it perfectly. It stopped my heart. Came along the street at a slow march, a single individual—a stark, naked man, drum beating—followed by no-one, preceded by no-one, his arms folded like he was bored, or waiting for someone.

The drum was his heart beating.

Which all could hear.

The Grandmother and Grandfather of Middatun Town clapped solemnly, the grandmother yawning. Middatun Town. Midleton. Myriad streets with nothing at all lining them. No pubs, no shops. A population of thirty thousand that were drowned and never born. Buildings as high as the sky with nothing in them only shadows. The old are young, the young are old. A tractor to every woman but no-one to pull a smoking wreck from a field or lift a fallen person to their feet. Four pubs for the kids and eleven empty schools. One church only, filled with politicians. The river runs in a straight line up the Main Street, the river filled with hardcore and tarmacadam. Thirty thousand lost that were never found! The N25 splitting the town like an atom. Laughing children tossing their teddy bears into that river of a road. Every building a bouncy castle. I spoke the words and they bounced deliriously and fell away dizzy and exhausted and over-tired and stroppy. *Will you be in time for the parade?* The words spoken, but by whom and what for? We voted yes to a motion, I don't remember which one. My memory, bypassed... That town. Myself. Who knows what happens? We kept our eyes on the street; a drummer's pulse beat out; the old couple clapping their little hands off, lost in their overcoats, their skin pale and smooth and rosy and unblemished. I clapped and cheered as the drummer came down, followed by thirty-five tractors. I was a believer then, but then I fell to sit on the hard hot cold frozen pavement, to take a little rest. No one in the crowd around me had feet. Ten thousand around me, and I alone on my arse, looking up, seeing only the hard shoulder of a long road. I feel the grit in my hands even now. I would go, I thought, to the boat in the centre of the roundabout on the outskirts of Middatun Town. I would be safe there, for only the roundabouts and the roads were real. As I rose and fled under the blazing sun, back the way I'd come, the signs of the town and the road were too dark to see. Not a soul would look above or beneath them. Not a soul would. And then the lorries came, and the machines, and the noise—

SATORI
Maria Isakova Bennett

I'm in darkness, but see clearly:
a sardonyx chalice set with jewels,

a cobbled road to the docks,
trucks unloading in the early hours,

puddles in the street, their surface
bodhrán tight, a dimpled pattern

of tearfall keeping time
with my mother's broken breaths.

It's the jewels that remain—
rubies that beat *vivace* like the heart

after running; and cool sapphires
like winter skies rinsed clean,

like a prayer of thanksgiving—
set before Christ Pantocrator.

Reading 'A Song' by Goethe
Astrid Alben

The high-speed train clears Dover into the tunnel cutting through sediments laid down some hundred million years ago. It's Gobi desert dark when the overhead lights pop on. Poet draws in closer to the window. As he draws in closer his eyes and nose touch the point of condensation. Poet tells me he will only ever know himself as an image sliding back and forth between degrees of being there. Not introspection but retrospection and that, Poet says, is why Goethe, two months before he died, visited the mountain hut at Ilmenau on whose walls he'd carved some fifty, yes fifty years before, that in all trees hardly a breath stirs. This was in 1832, the year in which the first hydrographical survey of the channel was conducted. Nothing stirs here. As the train pummels through the darkness Poet's image swings limpidly in and out of focus. At some hundred and fifty feet below the seabed Poet believes himself to be passing right underneath his life with the earth out of reach above him. Poet says he has slipped off the radar of his existence. He is without his end knowing where to find him. Elsewhere is radio static, mechanical toys and the oblivion of the tides. Elsewhere Poet tells me across the aisle unanswered letters uproot cathedrals. And wait, Poet says said Goethe, you too shall rest before long.

I Am My Own North Star
Lily Cook

I am a maiden name
on a government document.

I am on a run,
in the park,   alone at night.

I am the name   inside the tattooed heart,
stick 'n' poked,
on my own chest.

I am the mammographer,
checking my own breast.

I am Geraldine Santoro,
I am Plath's heart beating:
"I am, I am..."

a saguaro on fire in Phoenix,
a china cup behind glass
on Park Ave
sipping chamomile, chugging Stella
a wet dream, a nightmare,

expansive,   expanding.

THE FACE OF A FISH OR THE PROBLEM OF TRANSFORMATION
Yoko Towada

Where does the face of a fish begin and where does it end? This question occurred to me when I was standing in a fishing boat near the Lofoten Islands. A fish almost as big as a sewing machine had just been hauled out of the water. I looked into his staring eyes. The fish, through his mouth and gills, through the heaving of his flanks covered with wet-glistening scales, breathed heavily, irregularly, and furiously. The whole body of the fish made-up a face. The word "face", according to the definition of a (German) dictionary, means "the face, nose, and mouth of the human head from the chin to the hairline." But where is the front of a fish's head? I asked myself. A fish has a face, but no front.

As I read the definition in the dictionary, I was surprised that it referred explicitly to a "human" head. The idea of a fish having a face is misplaced if the German word 'face' can only be used in relation to people. Although I had learned that the mouth of a dog is called *Maul* and that the word *wohnen* (to dwell, to live) cannot be used for animals, it had never occurred to me that a fish could not have a face.

But a face really has to be something other than just a part of the body. This impression came home to me when I read the following passage by Walter Benjamin. It's about children who passionately collect various objects.

"Untidy Child. Every stone he finds, each flower picked, and every butterfly caught is for him already the start of a collection, and everything he owns makes up a huge collection. In him, this passion shows its true face, the austere Indian look, which in antiquarians, scientists and bibliomaniacs smoulders manically and murkily. As soon as this passion comes to life, he is a hunter. He hunts the souls whose traces he detects in things; between souls and things, years pass in which his field of vision remains free of people. It is as if he lives in a dream. He gets to know nothing lasting; everything happens to him as if by chance. His years of wandering are hours in a dream forest."[1]

Benjamin does not say that the face of a collector expresses his passion, but rather, passion in a collector shows its face. In doing so, the human body acts as a medium

---

1   Walter Benjamin *One Way Street*

through which passion can be fully visible. A facescape, free of humanity, can be like a canvas that receives and projects pictures. So I came to a new definition of the face: a face is something that becomes visible.

Just as passion has a face, so too does a city have one or more faces. Walter Benjamin reads such faces: faces that take on feeling, faces of a city or an object. Apparently, faces do not appear on their own, but appear only when they are read. There are people who are obsessively preoccupied with collecting certain items and reading their faces. One such person, namely a passionate doll collector, Benjamin has designated as a physiognomist of the world of things. When Benjamin speaks of physiognomy, he does not regard faces as expressions of a person's "inner truth", as Johann Caspar does; whose work still strongly shapes common ideas of physiognomy.

In Lavater's physiognomy, faces are typed and classified to bestow moralistic character traits to the owner of the face. A body's capacity for metamorphosis is negated by such concepts. According to Lavater's physiognomy, it is also unthinkable that a face always reflects something alien.

When Benjamin speaks of physiognomy, he has a completely different take. As a physiognomist Benjamin reads the faces of objects, visions or even architecture as ambiguous texts. By describing them, things are transformed into literary texts.

In a contribution designed as a radio programme for children and adolescents, Benjamin describes ETA. Hoffmann as a physiognomist, who read the demonic faces of the city of Berlin and made them known abroad.

"Like many great poets, he (Hoffmann.) was so fated that he did not see the extraordinary as floating freely in space, but rather in particular people, things, houses, objects, streets, and so on. As you may have heard, people who look at other people's faces, at the way they walk, their hands, the shape of their heads, in order to determine their character or profession or fate, are called physiognomists . So Hoffmann was less of a seer than an auditor. That is the German translation of *Physiognomiker.*"[2]

The ghosts, spirits or demons that appear in Hoffmann's literature are the embodiment of the demonic features found in the faces of a city.

A face, a sound, a smell, a taste, a feeling. The German words used to name sensual perceptions always seemed strange to me. Hearing is the ability to hear, while odour is not about the ability to smell but the reek of scent. What does the phrase "I smell" mean? Does smell emanate from me or do I perceive smell? Equally ambiguous is taste. I taste. Do I taste a flavour or am I tasted by a carnivore? If odour is called smell and flavour is called taste, that which is seen may be called a "face" (translator's note, *Gesicht* — the German word for 'face' has the same root as the word *gesehen* 'seen').

---

2   *Demonic Berlin*

What I like about other people is what I call a face. The face is therefore not an anatomically fixable body part, because you can see a face in a hand or in handwriting or in the way a head nods.

Faces are everywhere, yet you can often not recognize a face. For example, it is hard to really 'see' a conversation partner's face. In his eyes, I see my own facial expression reflected: my restlessness, timidity, defiance, aversion, shyness, etc. At this sight, I feel embarrassed by the way I hear a recording of my own voice, and I have to look away immediately. It is therefore unbearable to look into the eyes of the interlocutor. In such a situation, I would like to close my eyes and only perceive the images that become visible through words and breath, just as one hears a radio play.

There are also people with faces that appear on their shoulder, on their chest, between their fingers or even on their stomach. These faces clearly express something to me because, unlike eyes, they do not reflect me as I look at them.

Does voice have a face? In this question, I come to a transformation story in *Metamorphoses* by Ovid, in which Echo is rejected by Narcissus and turns into a voice. Interestingly, Echo is portrayed as an invisible creature even before the transformation. She could have received a visible form through the eyes of a lover. Instead, she is rejected and remains bodiless. The transformation of Echo is not about a physical change, but rather about the emergence of the meaning of echo as we use it today. It transforms into a concept and thereby becomes bodiless.

In the story, Echo survives as a voice. By contrast, Narcissus, who has fallen in love with his own reflection, loses his voice. Both characters are somewhat identical: Echo is a voice that can only repeat what another voice has said. And Narcissus desires his mirror image, which is the repetition of his own body. He complains about the futility of this wilfulness: "for I would fain put off this mortal form; which only means I wish the object of my love away."[3] Echo manages to insert a small shift in the repetition and so change the meaning. As Narcissus tells her: "I would rather die than belong to you," Echo repeats only the last part of the sentence: "belong to you". The meaning of the statement is thereby reversed. In this way, Echo can articulate herself while Narcissus transforms into a dumb flower.

When I discovered the word "I" (*ich*) in the middle of the word "face" (*Gesicht*), I came up with the idea that the face could be the peculiarity of the verb "I": "I have it." What could this sentence mean? As far as my face is concerned, I have not done anything that I could tell in the perfect form. I have not finished writing my face yet. Above all, I have not even seen my face, just its reflection. At this thought, I wrote the following text:

"Since I was born in this world, I have never seen my face from the outside. No mirror shows me how I look in conversation with another person. Often I see puzzling

3   *Metamorphoses* Ovid

features in another's face. They fascinate me, and I reflect them on my face. My face is a sketchbook. The person who speaks to me sees drawings of my own features in my face and enters them, just as you get into a train. I do not know how I look from the outside. From inside, I have seen my face many times: a shady landscape with a marshy forest and two frozen lakes. There is also a stalactite cave and two tunnels with shells in the net. I enter this landscape and run away.

I cannot see that woman's face from the inside. So I become a wind and stroke the surface of her face. Her face is a deserted landscape. The wind reads the Braille written in the fields. At that moment two lakes appear in the panorama. To feel one's way is seeing without distance. When it blows, blonde grasses and gray-blue waters rush. In the stalactite cavern, from out of which the blind wind blows, lives a naked monster with reddish, damp skin. The ground is sticky, wet and glistens blood red. The monster's abdomen has attached to the ground. It does not growl, does not howl, does not speak. When the beast moves, however, a moaning wind is made. It flies out of the cave and transforms itself into words.

A blind wind arises out of one landscape and moves itself into another. Then it returns or moves on to a third landscape. The wind doesn't belong in any one place. It stops suddenly, and then it blows again. Is this wind different from the last? How can you tell one gust from another? Does a wind have a face? I see the wind's face when the water shows laughter lines or makes faces. I see its face when the last leaf on the tree shakes its head. The wind's face is what it sets in motion."[4]

It is most commonly considered a bad thing in Germany, if you have multiple faces. In Christian paintings, only characters who embody evil have several faces. For example, in a 15th century painting, 'The Last Judgement' by Stefan Lochner,[5] I see a greenish being with faces on his shoulders, stomach and knees. His arms resemble dragon legs, the ears of a devil grow out of his head, and out of his mouth a dog's tongue stretches. The creature tries, with its claws at the Last Judgement to catch naked people who want to head towards the heavenly gates, dragging and pulling themselves. On the left half of the picture you can see angels escorting happy people to Heaven. Each angel has only one face. Amazingly, I have never seen a picture that depicts Jesus, God, or an angel with multiple faces. In Buddhist art, however, there are often statues with multiple faces. For example, Senjukan'non – a creature that appears in various guises to save people – is usually depicted as a figure that has 42 hands and 11 or 27 faces. In all his hands – except the front two – he has an eye. The existence of many eyes is combined with the gift of Kan'non to be able to observe many people at the same time and everywhere (the name for the figure Kan'non in Sanskrit is "Avalokites'vara" – "to observe with a cheerful eye").

---

4   Yoko Tawada *But the mandarins must be robbed tonight*

5   I thank Anne Duden for the postcard with this picture

The large number of hands is said to signify the ability to save many people. And the existence of several faces demonstrates the great art of transformation.

You can hardly avoid the theme of the face, when you deal with the foreign. Travellers obtain so many masks for their faces from the locals because otherwise they would be invisible. There is a scene in my story "Das Bad", in which the protagonist returns to Japan after a long stay in Europe. The mother looks at her in surprise and asks: "Why do you have such an Asian face?"
The protagonist responds: "What are you saying, mother? It's obvious, I am an Asian girl." Then the mother says:
"I don't mean it like that. You 've acquired a weird face; like the Japanese who appear in American films."[6]
Observers, by their expectations, create masks, which graft onto the flesh of strangers. Thus, the eyes of the other are always inscribed on your own face. A face can develop multiple layers. Maybe you can flip a face like a travelogue.

Sometimes foreign faces are translated like foreign words, not only on a person's head but also in a photograph, for example. Roland Barthes comments on his photograph, which appeared in a Japanese newspaper, as follows:
"This Western lecturer is experiencing Japaneseization when the Kobe Shinbun newspaper portrays him; Nippon's typography makes his eyes narrower, his eyebrows blacker."[7]
Once in New York, an American photographer told me that my author's headshot looked like that of a German writer. Since then, I have taken a closer look at author headshots on US books and I have actually found differences from German photographs. In American books, an author is often portrayed as a normal person: as one who can also be a reader's neighbour. By contrast, the face of an author in a German photograph is portrayed as a historic wall that cannot be broken because it no longer exists. Her skin becomes covered with a sacred layer and thus she appears unapproachable.

The fear of hypocrisy forces her mouth to show ill humour. Her eyes also shine critically and narcissistically at the same time, as if the author wanted to tell her reader: But I do not write for you. In an author's photograph, a face embodies the idea of authorship as it is produced in a specific culture. In this respect, faces are written and not shown.

In Ovid's *Metamorphoses* the first chapter relates, in a way, the origin of the world, which is at the same time an explanation for the transmutability of individual beings. The idea that one being can transform itself into another comes from a memory of the time

6   Yoko Tawada *The Bathroom*
7   Roland Barthes *The Empire of Signs*

when the form of living beings and things were not yet set.

"There was earth, water and air; but you could not stand on the ground, you could not swim through the waves, and the air was without light. Nothing was left to it's own form; one thing stood in the way of the other, because in one and the same body cold struggled with hot, wet with dry, soft with hard, weightless with heavy. This dispute was settled by God and by better nature. For he separated the earth from heaven and the waters from the earth, and he separated the clear sky from the dense air."[8]

God then created the world by setting limits to chaos. His work was quite a linguistic achievement. Because materially one cannot separate the waters from the earth, since water always contains some earth and vice versa. Only speech-terms can be used to separate both and say, here is the water and here is the earth. The word "earth" says nothing about what the earth actually is, but the word just makes it clear that the earth is not a body of water; there is no sky, no air, etc. The transformation stories in *Metamorphoses* may appear to be fairy tales, fictitious, fantastic in the sense of unrealistic, in the eyes of Realists. But the book of *Metamorphoses* only points out that the definitions are fictitious.

In *Metamorphoses*, gods and humans are transformed into monsters, animals or plants for various reasons. For example, in Daphne's transformation into a tree, her transformation was a method of self-defence. Because Apollo fell in love with her and wanted to force her to marry him, while she desired no man. Iphis, who was raised as a boy and fell in love with a woman, was turned into a man. Tiresias also experienced sex change;, he encountered two snakes in a forest and beat them with a stick. That's how he turned into a woman. After seven years, he met the same snakes again, struck them again and turned back into a man. In Actaeon, from whose forehead "strange antlers" grew, the transformation had the character of a punishment. He looked at the naked Diana while bathing and was transformed by her into a half-animal. Neptune turned into a bull, a ram, a bird and a dolphin, depending on which woman he wanted to seduce. For him, transformation is nothing but a love art. The grounds for transformation is made clear by Ovid every time.

Unlike *Metamorphoses*, Kafka's 'Metamorphosis' never tells us why Gregor Samsa transforms. After reading the story of Daphne, it seems likely that Gregor Samsa has turned into a bug so he won't have to go on a business trip. His transformation would then be an act of liberation from an oppressive way of life, to which one would be delivered without it. If Gregor Samsa, were Actaeon's descendant, it would be a punishment. Maybe he was watching his own sister take a bath, and his father reproaches him by throwing apples at him. By so doing, his father wants to remind him of the famous apple of paradise, or the phrase "throwing somebody with rotten apples" motivated him to do this. The sister could not save her enchanted brother, unlike the sisters to be found in the 'Seven Ravens' and many other fairy tales. It is only a guess that Gregor Samsa's

8 Ovid *Metamorphoses*

transformation was intended as a punishment. The text does not even name the law he is alleged to have transgressed. The unnamed law shapes the empty centre of the story.

In the fairy tale there are two types of transformation. Either a human being is transformed into an animal – this does not happen out of free will, but when a person comes under a spell – or else an animal transforms into a human being, and by its own volition. In many Japanese fairy tales, an animal transforms into a woman and marries a human being. Later she turns back and leaves the man again. There are just as many fairy tales in which animals turn into men and marry women, but in the fairy-tales still known today, man, who is in reality an animal, is always a woman. Such fairy tales supposedly also existed in the European cultural area, but were banned because of the prohibition of sodomy from memory. For someone who marries an animal in the form of a human being, transgresses the law. The reverse case, on the other hand, is less problematic. If a frog kissed by a woman is in reality a human being, that is not considered sodomy. But I doubt now whether this phenomenon is actually due only to the Christian prohibition of sodomy. In Ovid's *Metamorphoses*, there is no case in which an animal transforms into a human being. The absence of such narratives must have other reasons, even if it applies to Greek mythology.

Transformation is the dream of many artists. There is a famous transformation story by a Japanese writer from the 18th century named Ueda Akinari. This story tells of a monk who was known as a painter and always painted fish. He often went to Lake Biwa, gave the fishermen money and asked them to release the fish they had just caught. He then painted the fish as they swam joyfully away in the water with their regained freedom. Once he became very ill and lay in bed for a long time. His soul separated from him and wandered through villages, over rivers and mountains, until it finally reached the familiar Lake Biwa. The painter, who had never been familiar with the waters, felt like swimming and entered the waters. There he was led by a big fish to the water god. The god transformed the painter into a carp, so that he could swim even more freely. The carp was soon caught by humans. If the painter, who was still in bed, had not woken up and sent a messenger to the kitchen where the carp was to be killed and cooked, he would have died. The painter lived for a very long time. Shortly before he died, he took several carp pictures that he had painted and sank them in the lake. There, the painted carp, of paper and silk, dissolved and romped happily in the water.[9]

An artist can identify himself with the model of his writing through a humble occupation with process. However, in order to produce his writing, he must simultaneously distance himself from it. After his work is completed, the possibility of transformation is excluded. In science, the work of research must consistently maintain

9   Akinari Ueda *Under the Rainy Moon*

distance from the research object. A zoologist must not turn into an animal. But how can a scientist be sure that he will never change? Since Japanese and African ethnologists are now allowed to have a say about their own cultures, it would also be desirable if zoology could be researched from the perspective of animals.

For this reason, animals should first turn into humans. This radical form of science must have interested Kafka. His story 'Investigations of a Dog' is an example of such a science. In another story by Kafka, 'A Report to an Academy' the first-person narrator is a monkey caught in the Gold Coast. On the ship, in his cage and later in a new land, he learns everything that makes up the existence of a human being: from spitting to drinking alcohol, from making money to talking about himself. Now, it says in the text, he has separated from 'Monkeydom'. Kafka has presented a new form of science here: research objects are transformed into researchers. He bears scars on his body – memories of the time in which he was still treated like an experimental object. Therefore, the researcher can still look at certain peculiarities of people with the necessary distance, for example, the concept of freedom that people long for.

"… with freedom, one cheats oneself too often among people And as freedom is to the most exalted feelings, so too is the corresponding deception to the sublime."[10]

Freedom was never available to the 'I-Monkey', he was just looking for a way out. He had no choice but to train himself in the manners of humans and to carry out their so-called "progress" in order to get out of his cage. After he has made the transformation, he remembers how he was sitting in a cage. Without painful fear, he cannot think about the past, but at least he survives the transformation – unlike Gregor Samsa, who died as a bug.

The buzzword 'identity-loss' has replaced the concept of transformation. However, since antiquity – be it Greek or Chinese – transformation has been one of the most important motifs in literature. Poetic transformations form a space between the longing for a deadly transformation into an animal and the horror of transformation into a human being.

Originally published in *Verwandlungen* Konkursbuch Verlag, Tübingen, 2018

Translated from the German by Patrick Cotter

---

10   Franz Kafka *Stories*

Poem Ending with an Imitation of a Line from Philippe Jaccottet
James Owens

Hold this. Windows down, throwing strawberry stems
from the car, you and I drive the ruts by Cutler Lake,
moaning with pleasure as the sun-sugared berries
shiver, burst, and dissolve, the best just now starting to blet.

Hold this. A goldfinch flits and dodges. We scent woodsmoke
like foreknowledge of autumn. And swathes of the cold water,
watching wisely through birch trunks as we skirt the shore,
are as dark-sifting blue and deep-memoried as soot.

Hold this. Just as you lift a bitten berry by the stem
to praise, "It's like drinking life from a goblet,"
I ask, in the dim guard booth at the top of my spine,
some wordless question that might translate as "Why death?"

For answer, from the roadside: *vetch, trefoil, curled dock.*

VIENNA
James O'Sullivan

My fingers count black spots,
that strange mould
that spreads throughout this place,
wherever there is water,
even in the fridge,
when it gets too warm,
and frost begins to run.
I have taken shelter in the shower—
everything seems normal
with the spray upon my face,
Jim White in the background,
beyond, some other rattle,
the news, a playlist.
I just can't see it, you had said,
maybe we need some time apart.
I had stayed away too long,
chasing dreams
of Rome and Vienna—
you were *always* in those visions,
sat on the edge of some square,
sipping your lungo,
a cigarette balanced in your hand.
In the evenings
we would neck Tuscan wine,
thinking that was our thing,
rushing hurriedly along ancient streets,
like the dead given a chance to live again.

FALLING OFF THE PERIODIC TABLE
Elizabeth Murawski

Searching desperately
for things to say,

the gap too wide
to swim across,

I tread water, wonder
if he does the same,

or if it doesn't matter
when one has tried so long

and failed, the raw cord
connecting us

like an astronaut's
to the mother ship

severed. So that
we drift and bob

through space, both
children now, afraid

our cries will go
unheard, unanswered.

Photo: John Minihan

THE SOUTHWORD INTERVIEW
Matthew Sweeney, Poet

Matthew Sweeney was born in Lifford, Co. Donegal, Ireland in 1952. He moved to London in 1973 and studied at the Polytechnic of North London and the University of Freiburg. After living in Berlin and Timisoara for some years, he returned to Ireland and now lives in Cork.

His poetry collections include *A Dream of Maps* (Raven Arts Press, 1981), *A Round House* (Raven Arts Press, 1983), *The Lame Waltzer* (Raven Arts Press, 1985), *Blue Shoes* (Secker & Warburg, 1989), *Cacti* (Secker & Warburg, 1992), *The Bridal Suite* (Jonathan Cape, 1997) *A Smell of Fish* (Jonathan Cape, 2000), *Selected Poems* (Jonathan Cape, 2002), *Sanctuary* (Jonathan Cape, 2004), *Black Moon* (Jonathan Cape, 2007), *The Night Post: A Selection* (Salt, 2010); and three from Bloodaxe, *Horse Music* (2013), *Inquisition Lane* (2015) and *My Life as a Painter* (2018). *Black Moon* was shortlisted for the T.S. Eliot Prize and for the Irish Times Poetry Now Award. *Horse Music* won the inaugural Pigott Poetry Prize in association with Listowel Writers' Week, and is a Poetry Book Society Recommendation. He has also published editions of selected poems in Canada (*Picnic on Ice,* Vehicle Press, 2002) and and two translated by Jan Wagner in Germany, *Rosa Milch* (Berlin Verlag, 2008) and *Hund und Mond* (Hanser Berlin, 2017). *King of a Rainy Country*, versions of Baudelaire's prose poems appeared this year.

He won a Cholmondeley Award in 1987 and an Arts Council Writers' Award in 1999. He has also published poetry for children, with collections including *The Flying Spring Onion* (1992), *Fatso in the Red Suit* (1995) and *Up on the Roof: New and Selected Poems* (2001). His novels for children include *The Snow Vulture* (1992) and *Fox* (2002). He edited *The New Faber Book of Children's Poems* (2003) and *Walter De la Mare: Poems* (2006) for Faber; co-edited *Emergency Kit: Poems for Strange Times* (Faber, 1996) with Jo Shapcott; and co-wrote *Writing Poetry* (Teach Yourself series, Hodder, 1997) and the comic novel *Death Comes for the Poets* (Muswell Press, 2012) with John Hartley Williams.

Matthew Sweeney has held residencies at the University of East Anglia and the South Bank Centre in London, and was Poet in Residence at the National Library for the Blind as part of the Poetry Places scheme run by the Poetry Society in London. He was writer-in-residence at University College Cork in 2012-13, and is a member of Aosdána.

When did you know you wanted to be a poet?

My father was the principal in the primary school in Malin I went to, and he read poems aloud to the class. I remember being entranced by Yeats's early fairy poems, and ghost poems such as Walter de la Mare's 'The Listeners'. I loved the way poems were mysterious and dramatic, had a nice noise to them, and could tell a story in a very short space. When I went on to the boarding school in Gormanston I soon began to love some of the work of the Romantic poets I encountered in class, and I began trying to write poems myself – sometimes piggybacking on a favourite poem, such as once on Coleridge's ghost poem, ' Christabel'. That was to learn something of the craft needed in writing poems. I used to destroy these efforts soon after writing them but not before showing them to one or two other boys who were also producing poems. One time I kept three of my efforts to give to my Head of English but he barely glanced at them, before returning them to me, saying poetry was something one grew out of. I then stopped writing poems, concentrating on science subjects, and after the Leaving I went to UCD to study Chemical Engineering. In my second year I began reading poems again and even possibly writing them, I can't remember exactly. I do recall spending the day in the library before a big physics exam engrossed in two long poems by Lord Byron, 'Beppo' and 'Don Juan', instead of looking at physics books. And that evening I phoned my father saying I was quitting college. He was annoyed and demanded to know why. Because I want to be a poet, I said.

But that wasn't the end of college for you?

No, but before I went back to college, another important bit of learning happened. After UCD I went to London, and pretty soon was installed in a flat-share in Maida Vale. Among the people living there was an art student from Monaghan called Joe Mallon, with whom a few years later, I began to co-edit the poetry broadsheet, *Cracked Lookingglass*, which ran for eight issues. We were helped to get this up and running by Eddie Linden who lived locally and edited the poetry magazine, *Aquarius*. Through Eddie I met the Scottish poet Aonghas MacNeacail or Angus Nicolson, as I knew him. I can't recall how, but Angus became my mentor. I took to visiting him once a week, bringing a bottle of wine or, more probably, cider, and my latest poems, of course. 'So you think you've written a masterpiece', Angus would say, as he took his red pen out. 'This bit sounds nice, doesn't it, but if you follow it into a corner, does it stand up? No, it doesn't'. A red X would go through the offending line, as we moved on to the next poem. Angus advised me to pin above my writing table a note containing the following advice: 'Unless you're prepared to write shite you'll never write a masterpiece'. It was all excellent advice, although I mightn't have known it then – I was sometimes a bit teary as I made my way home. I can see now that the discipline he was drumming into me came straight from the practice of William Carlos Williams, which is an inspired way to learn the craft needed to fashion a poem.

I was at this time doing dead-end draughtsman jobs, using some of my experience of being an engineering student. It was dull stuff, to say the least – how do you make the central heating plans for the newly created town of Milton Keynes interesting? For something different I took to selling hot dogs in the West End from a barrow picked up from dodgy Cypriot characters in a dingy place in Covent Garden. You just wheeled the barrow to your allotted pitch and sold as many awful hot dogs and burgers as you could, keeping an eye out for coppers who tried to nick you – there was no question of getting licences for this work. My pitch was just off Haymarket, on a side road where the artists' entrance of Her Majesty's Theatre was. The big poster on the wall showed a picture of Lauren Bacall who was in a show there at the time, and one afternoon Miss Bacall got out of a taxi and grabbed a hot dog from me before going into the theatre.

Despite such adventures I began to want to go back to college, to study English and German this time. I found out, though, that the English system of applying to colleges was pretty complicated. I knuckled down to it, nevertheless, and applied to five universities, four in London, one in Lancaster in the north, where my cousin Mary Molloy was studying, and I'd been impressed with the place when I'd visited her there. The upshot of my multi application was that none of the London universities accepted my Irish Leaving results (which were pretty good, seven honours, I think). Lancaster were fine with the Irish results but I felt I didn't want to leave London. I was getting used to the idea of giving up the dream of college when someone told me about the new polytechnics. So around the start of term I pitched up at the arts wing of the North London Polytechnic in Kentish Town where I had an interview with the formidable Mrs Sondergard. Not that it was a conventional interview at all. I was asked why I wanted to do English and we spoke about the poetry of Sylvia Plath for ten minutes. *Why German?* was the next question, and we spoke about Kafka. I then produced a handful of my poems which she read, before telling me I was just the kind of student the North London Polytechnic wanted. So I was officially a student again, a little wiser in the ways of the world this time.

Were you publishing in 'recognised' journals at this stage or did that come later?

No, small magazines in England and Ireland and one or two further afield. I did win a couple of lesser prizes, including a runner up or consolation prize in the 1980 National Poetry Competition – I remember it brought me £50 which I used to buy the ingredients for the Xmas dinner, including a small turkey from the market. And I did publish two pamphlets towards the end of my time at college, one with the Leicester based small magazine, *Omens*, the other with the London based *Oasis* – this second pamphlet contained mainly poems written during my year abroad in Freiburg, showing the influence of German poets I'd been reading, especially Peter Huchel.

At what stage did your first book come out?

I felt under self-imposed pressure to bring out my first collection before I was thirty, I don't know why. I remember doing a well-attended reading somewhere in Dublin in the late 70s, and afterwards I was approached by Thomas Kinsella who said some nice things but also advised me not to be in a hurry to publish my first book too soon. Wise advice but I disregarded it. I felt, ridiculously, that because all the poems in the collection I had cobbled together had been published in one magazine or another, then it naturally followed that the collection must come out. It was doing the rounds of the English publishers but no one was biting – the closest I came was, I think, Chatto and Windus. So I sent it to Ireland where it was done by Raven Arts Press. I have long thought that book to be a bit of a mistake. I see too many undigested influences there – Auden, WS Graham, Mark Strand. And the whole is too big, taking on subjects that are too vast for me to control at that stage. Straining after significance, tending towards portentousness. Not understanding yet that the best way to be serious was through a use of humour, something I should already have learned at that stage from Kafka. The second collection, I promised myself, would be much smaller in terms of the kind of poems I would aim at. And whether it was that gain in control, or simply the fact that my poems and name were gradually getting out there, I started to find more success with the magazines I tried. That second book, *A Round House*, has among the acknowledgements listed, *BBC Radio 3 (Poetry Now)*, *LRB*, *New Statesman*, *TLS*.

Another problem with that first book was I left out the best, most distinctive poems. These were a series of what I called 'Moonpoems', written in London during the punk period. I remember some years later showing these to John Hartley Williams and he said he liked them much better than the poems in my first book. He was right. What had happened there – a failure of nerve? 'Well, I had earlier sent a collection to Gallery for consideration which was mainly made up of the 'Moonpoems'. This earned a two page detailed rejection, the gist of which, I remember, was that paranoia was no subject for poetry. I think while I must have blanked this submission in the main, it left its mark, and probably prompted the demotion of the 'Moonpoems'. For example, it was these that were supposed to comprise the *Oasis* pamphlet but at the last minute I switched them for some of the German-influenced poems. A selection of them finally saw the light of day in the bootleg book I published with Salt in 2000, under the title *The Night Post*.

Oh, I remember one other thing, a lost book. After my first collection Dolmen wanted to do the next one. I gave them a manuscript and all seemed to be on course, but then Liam Miller died. It still looked like it would happen but sadly it didn't, I don't remember the details why. Half or so of this lost book are in the second book that did come out, but the other half simply vanished from the record.

Clearly by The Round House *you felt you had found your voice. Did you see yourself as still writing within the Irish/British tradition or were you aware of veering away from it under the influence of the Germans and others?*

Yes, I think my voice is there in *The Round House.* I certainly am more comfortable with that book than the first one, although the first time I was aware I'd found my voice was with a poem in that first book. The poem is 'Last Supper', and is the only poem from the collection included in my Cape *Selected.* Reading through that second book again now, I couldn't say I detect a strong German or European strain yet, except maybe in a handful of poems towards the end, 'New Town', 'That Place', 'Preparation for Survival', 'The Servant', maybe 'The Dancehall'. But who am I to say? The writer is often the least aware of what's going on.

With two books behind you, you still attended workshops.

I was involved with two poetry workshops in London during the late 80s or early 90s, I can't be sure of the dates. The first was in Notting Hill, at the home of Robert Greacen in Pembridge Crescent. Robert had attained some prominence in the early 1940s, but had been quiet for a number of years till he brought out, in the late 70s, I think, a spritely book called *A Garland for Captain Fox* with Gallery. I enjoyed the fun and playfulness of these poems and went to call on Robert. The workshop grew out of this meeting. The participants of this workshop were a mixed bunch, including some people who had very limited success in the 40s or 50s (one man's sole success was a poem in the *New Statesman* back then), and some younger people who were beginning or threatening to emerge. Names I can give include an old friend of Robert's, Jenny Joseph, Vicki Feaver, Aidan Murphy, Michael Foley (who accused a poem of mine under discussion one night of being riddled with Berryman), Cahal Dallat, Tim Dooley and James Sutherland Smith. James was a bit of a fierce critic, and if he declared your poem to be 'a splendid piece' that was praise indeed. Once he decreed a poor chap's poem to be the worst he'd ever seen in his life. Sometimes Irish poets who were in town came along as guest poets – once, I think, John F. Deane came. This workshop chugged along for a number of years, meeting once a month or so, everyone bringing a bottle of cider which gradually changed to a bottle of wine. Then Robert moved to Dublin and the workshop ceased.

After a lapse of time to allow me to lose the deadwood from the previous incarnation I took over the workshop. I asked a handful of people from Robert's sessions to join the new operation – Vicki, Cahal and Tim came, James had moved to Saudi Arabia, I think. I also invited a bunch of poets who were beginning to make a name – including Michael Donaghy, Jo Shapcott, Sarah Maguire, Don Patterson, Eva Salzman, Ruth Padel, Maurice Riordan, Lavinia Greenlaw. The workshop first met in my flat in Dombey Street till my then wife complained, so we moved to having it in an upstairs room in The Lamb pub in Lamb's Conduit Street, where Ted Hughes and Sylvia Plath had courted. It was the perfect place to meet – we tended to convene on a Saturday afternoon every two months or so. The workshop became known as the Lamb Workshop. The criticism was lively – I had instigated a system of the poems being presented anonymously, which seemed to encourage people to be forthright in their assessments. It also allowed one to be savage about one's own poem, if one felt the need for that. At any case, if one emerged from that workshop having had a poem praised, that was cause for celebration. It's exactly how a workshop should be, in my opinion. Too many workshops pussyfoot, and are too nice about the work discussed. At some stage I felt it was time to close down the workshop – it had run its course, I felt. A lot of the poets were starting to have high profiles, and their opinions were less and less open to other ways of writing, or so it seemed to me. Some people told me I was wrong. Anyway, a few years later I had a visit from two Mexican poets. They knew about the workshop and were publishing an anthology of British poems called *The Lamb Generation*. The world is truly small indeed.

Getting back to your idea that the best way to be serious was through a use of humour, can you elaborate? That belief doesn't stop you appreciating poets with very little humour such as Plath or Ní Chuilleanáin.

Or to take a more obvious example, Georg Trakl, whose work I love (Kafka was a fan too), but who I've heard poets say is depressing. In each of these three poets it's the visual imagery that I admire, and how that introduces strangeness or estrangement. Whether one employs humour – whether one allows it into the work is a personal matter, and dependent on the personality and upbringing of the writer. I could argue, say, that the fact that I grew up in Donegal made the use of humour a more pressing option. My granny, no literary lady, used to say she loved a joke with a jag in it. Strangers are often befuddled by dark Donegal humour – they don't get it, don't know how to react. So is it always with humour that's not overtly obvious. How many times have I heard that Germans have no sense of humour, and having lived more than five years in that country, I know that belief to be bunkum. I once came out of a brilliant staging of Beckett's *Waiting for Godot* in the Barbican, London, and the English couple leaving behind me were clearly unhappy and unamused. *Typical pretentious Irish drivel*, I heard the man mutter. To me Godot is a classic example of being serious through humour. And what that majestic play shows in spades is that the humour lets in human warmth. When I studied Kafka at the North London Polytechnic I was always in stitches in the seminars. *Why are you always laughing at Kafka?* another student asked me one day. *Yes, why do you find it funny?* the lecturer asked, following with an invitation to give a seminar showing the humour in Kafka. I'll give two seminars, I said, one to point out the humour, one to show how the humour makes it doubly serious. Once I was being interviewed for an English magazine, maybe *Magma*, and the interviewer wanted me to give him an example from life of that black humour. After a while I produced one – a night when I was involved in a poker game with a corpse at a wake. Some months later, after a lot of difficulty, I came up with a poem on the subject. It's called 'Poker', and I'm still fond of it – and it has loads of warmth. After all that, I should add that I myself have written many poems with no humour at all. It is never a necessity, only an option.

How would you respond to critics/editors who would dismiss your poems as 'whimsy' or 'inconsequential narratives'? There is a temptation not to respond at all, but what would you say to the curious, exploring reader who would be in danger of swallowing such critics' dismissiveness? Do you think your penchant for avoiding commentary and rhetorical flourishes contributes to this perception they have?

Yes, I have been accused of whimsy. It's usually English critics or editors. I have not encountered the criticism in Germany. Let's not forget also that it's not just the humour that bothers them, it's the wilful transgression into non-realism – what I call the weird zone. If your belief is that poetry should always be rational, realist, serious, well–mannered, autobiographical (and ideally perfectly metrical) then you're going to be horrified by the apparent wildness of the weird zone. I have never wanted rhetoric in my poetry, although I know some American poets use it well. To me it belongs in politics. And I don't want commentary either – I believe poetry should *show*, like film. I have no wish to be a critic of society, although one needs the matter of the world to obliquely find its own way into the work. Of course, this means that some people will never get on with what I do. So be it. I write what I'm meant to write, and there is more than one way to cook an egg. And maybe there will be one reader in the Orkneys who will value my work nevertheless. Of course, no one goes into the weird zone for the sake of being weird. It's to get a fresh angle – to fulfill Robert Frost's call for poetry to be a fresh look and a fresh listen. Kafka wasn't really writing about someone turning into a beetle in the story 'Metamorphosis'. Well, he was but he was writing about more too. It's a metaphor, and metaphor has always been the life blood of poetry. And it's best not to know what Kafka was writing about really.

Yes, the weird fires the imagination and something imaginative entertains. It's great to be entertained, isn't it? All serious entertainment transcends into art. People talk about how some of the best writing being done these days is being done for television, take Westworld *for instance, deep in the weird zone, full of mystery, and addressing important philosophical questions slantways — all the time, never forgetting to be entertaining; if it isn't entertaining it doesn't attract an audience, the money to be produced won't be forthcoming and ultimately the show does not get made. Do you think the need for entertainment value in contemporary poetry is underappreciated?*

We have to a bit careful here. I value entertainment in all areas of the arts but as regards poetry it's never the whole story. Well, Paul Durcan is entertaining and attracts large, appreciative audiences at his readings. So does Billy Collins, and Carol Ann Duffy, but they would all claim they're serious too — and I would agree. In the last decades of the last century the Liverpool Poets brought poetry a bit of the popularity of rock music. This didn't stop a lot of poets being sniffy about them. And aren't we straying, here, into the debate about page poetry and performance poetry? I don't think any poetry with a claim to being serious can just be entertaining, with the exclusion of anything else. And surely one of the things poetry has always been able to do is disturb the reader. I certainly believe in poetry doing this — asking uncomfortable questions of its audience. Of course, while it's doing this it can also be entertaining. Take a look at Browning's 'Porphyria's Lover'.

You have referred to the imagery in Plath being what attracts you and made a reference to film. Your work is undeniably very visual — it inspires images and scenes in the mind of the reader. What role do you think sound and music have to play?

The sound of a poem is vitally important, I agree, but I'm not one of those poets who value it above everything. We're not talking about piano concertos here. For me the most important of the senses for writing poetry is the visual sense. If one can visualise a scene or a narrative through imagery one is getting somewhere. Of course I want my poems to be euphonious, to be easy on the ear, to carry a music that can be buried — and devices such as alliteration, assonance, cadence, repetition, chorus, dramatic pauses, even rhyme, come into play here. And regular metre, if you want that. A poem has to be shaped well, and that goes for the noise of the poem too. I prefer jazz (contemporary European jazz, mainly) to classical music — it's more subtle in its effects. That's the way I want the music of my poems to work.

Tell me how a poem typically starts and develops for you.

A poem typically starts for me with an image, something that bubbles up from my unconscious. I then poke this around till it goes somewhere with its own alternative logic. I tend to know very little about the poems when I'm writing them, nor do I want to know much. I use my craft to shape what I'm writing into a poem – you could say that this is the conscious mind taking over but it's not quite. It's still working by instinct, without any worked out reasons, and is open to non-sequiturs or details that might surprise. This process even applies to commissions – in the old days I used to grapple with these in a conscious way and the result would be always leaden and flat, and embarrassing. Now if my unconscious plays ball I come up with something I can live with, and if not I lose the commission fee. Some poems sometimes get written by the conscious mind but invariably I go off these quickly and try to keep them out of my collections. Frost stressed the importance of surprise in poetry – it's a good idea to surprise yourself in your writing, he said; if you do that you might surprise your reader, which is always a good thing. Poetry is no place for obviousness or predictability.

How does your redrafting process go? Is is quick or drawn—out? Are there typically many changes from draft to draft or just tinkering?

One of the consequences of working from the unconscious is that there tends not to be a great deal of redrafting, as such. It would have to be described as tinkering, although there can be a fair bit of that, even as late as on the proofs of a collection. Sometimes a bit more is needed – a first attempt falls very flat, and a second stab has to get hold of the image or scenario in a much more thorough way. I have identified these failures as being too controlled by the conscious mind. The unconscious is a much more adroit fellow. In the worst cases the attempted poem comes to nothing whatsoever and gets abandoned. Even here, though, one may realise when working on a later poem that it is indeed a new attempt to write the failed poem – a second draft, then, even if somewhat belated and despite the fact it may have very little to do with the first draft. And there have been occasions along the way when I worked a poem to death in my notebook over months, really wanting to get it right, but it never happened. One time it was just after I'd delivered a collection to my publisher so I suppose I was trying or wanting to go in a new direction but wasn't ready to do so.

While you stopped bringing poems in progress to workshops you have shared poems, before publication, with trusted readers. How did/does that work?

One has to be careful who to show one's poems to. Or I should say what poets, as very few non-practitioners can talk in a meaningful way about the poetic craft. They have to be poets whose work you admire, and they should be people whose critical faculties you respect. And most of all they must get your work – be able to understand where you're coming from. Not all poets are able to do this, to be generous and open to another way of doing it, compared to how they write themselves. I saw in the workshops how this panned out. It make sense to keep the number of poets you give this special trust to quite small. And it's a good idea to be able to like them as people. Poets I've especially valued in this way would include my dead friend, greatly missed, John Hartley Williams, my partner, Mary Noonan, County Cork émigré, Maurice Riordan, my German translator, Jan Wagner, and the Canadian poet, David O'Meara. I've got what I can only call editing help from each of them. Writing poetry is a solitary, lonely activity and it's good to get back-up and support from people you trust before you offer your little creations to magazine editors, not all of whom will be open to your work, however many books you've published.

You have recently been very productive in producing prose poems. I believe you have been taken aback by their reception on this side of the Atlantic?

Yes, I was rather taken aback by the lack of interest in my prose poems from magazine editors and even from my regular publisher, Bloodaxe. It was if the whole enterprise was a mistake, or at least a bit of an embarrassing experiment. Still, some editors of decent periodicals saw what I was doing, which gave me heart. I remember sending Christopher Reid a link to a group of them available online. He was very positive, seeing the venture as an interesting development that would feed my poetry, and he suggested that overcoming entrenched English suspicion to the prose poem would be my most difficult challenge. He wondered if the United States would offer more rewarding possibilities. It is true that most of the prose poetry that comes into print is in the United States. but American prose poetry is its own kind of thing, and I've never been wildly enamoured of it. I was after something older – the spark came from Baudelaire's posthumously published collection of prose poems, *Le Spleen de Paris*.

Anyone who knows these will agree they read very differently to Baudelaire's celebrated poems collected in *Les Fleurs du Mal*. In fact, at first sight, it's hard to see how the prose things are poems at all. Baudelaire's own description of them was *petits poèmes en prose*. This doesn't mean that he went for a heightened or poetic prose. No, there's nothing poetic about these prose poems. And the range of them is wide – sometimes they're little stories or parables, other times meditations or epiphanies. They can simply be rants or paeans, or slightly extended japes, and yes, frequently they're funny, which his regular poems never are. Reading them, one never knew what was coming next. They are nothing like the contemporary American prose poem (however one might define that). Anyway, I took the decision to model my efforts as much as I could on Baudelaire's pieces, and strive for as wide a range as possible. Maybe, then, I should not have been so surprised at the lack of recognition of what I was trying to do. When the editor of *The Dark Horse* (a magazine that usually opens its doors to me) wrote that he wasn't sure about the prose poems, or even what distinguished them from short short stories, I replied, saying he probably would have said the same to Baudelaire.

Would you like to talk about the apparent aesthetic opening-up of the youngest generation of British poets and how this, perhaps, allows them to be more receptive to what you aim to do in your work?

Yes, there's been an opening out of the kind of poety some of the younger British poets are producing – I'm thinking of, for example, the new poets Faber are publishing, people like Emily Berry, Sam Reviere, Jack Underwood, and in Belfast, the newer poet, Stephen Sexton. What they're doing doesn't seem to be negating what I've tried to do, and indeed all of these young poets have shown interest in my work. I wish I could say the same for the young poets attaining prominence in Ireland but we won't go there. Nor am I talking about the performance poets published by some of the British presses, obviously to bring in money to the publishing venture. But the spirit of poetry and its possibilities seems to be more open over there, and that can only be a good thing.

How important have festival invitations been to you?

Festival appearances are vital for an active poet, particularly when a new book comes out (although I remember getting irritated when yet another festival told me they didn't want me because I had no new book out, as if it was the book that was important, and not the poet). In Britain, the big three poetry festivals were Ledbury, Stanza (in Scotland), and Aldeburgh – which introduced a limiting stipulation that poets could only appear there once, and more than one poet found this annoying. I was invited to the other two often enough, and there were some nice, smaller poetry festivals, such as Kings Lynn, in East Anglia, and the bigger literary festivals, such as Cheltenham, sometimes invited poets as fillers between the famous novelists. I had a nice arrangement with my then publisher, Cape – they would get me the festivals, if I lined up other readings. Ireland was another possible opening, with Cùirt in Galway being the big one, certainly in the beginning, but the best festival for poetry in Ireland in recent years is the Cork International Poetry Festival, without a doubt. And further afield, Poetry International in

Rotterdam and Harborfront in Toronto were exciting places to get invited to. Anyway, the profile-boost festival appearances bring are good for booksales (in theory, anyway), and even better for the poet's self-esteem and continuing belief in the work.

Tell us about your experience of being translated.

Around 2002 or 2003 I was invited to Germany from Romania to do a reading at a British Council conference in Potsdam. The captive audience was made up of academics from European universities. Two days after the reading I was approached by a man from Latvia who said: "Your poems are like little films. For two nights I have been unable to sleep because I keep seeing these films in my head. I am going to get you translated into Latvian so the people of Latvia can see these little films". As I didn't have much translated at this stage I was pleased to hear it. Sure enough, the book came about and I was invited to Riga to help it into the world with a few readings. First, though, there was the formal launch on some steps in an important looking square. An attractive TV actress read the title poem aloud (in English it's called 'The Bridal Suite' and opens like this: *On the third night in the bridal suite / without the bride, he panicked*). The actress spoke so much before she read the poem, making the audience titter, that I knew something was wrong. I soon found out that the translator (who wasn't at the event) hadn't known the English word 'suite', and had translated the line as '...the third night in the bridal suit...', making the poem ridiculous. The book in translation was immediately dead for me.

I'm starting with this cautionary tale to illustrate the care that has to be taken with translation, especially the translation of poetry, where every word is so exact. The ideal scenario is when the poet who's being translated is familiar with the language the poem is going into, and indeed I'm most comfortable being translated into German, which I studied at college. And I'm extremely fortunate to have an excellent translator in Jan Wagner, who happens to be a very fine poet, and, needless to say, it helps for a translator of poetry to be a poet him- or herself. As for how we approach the business of translation, first Jan sends me a list of questions or queries. Then I go through his draft translations with a fine tooth comb before sending off a list of questions of my own. So the whole process becomes something of a collaboration.

The joy of being translated (when it goes well) is that your work gets seen in a completely different context and culture. Sometimes the reaction to it can be quite different to the reaction it gets in its own culture. I heard Miroslav Holub say, for example, that he was much better received in the US and Britain than he was in his native Czechoslovakia, certainly at the end. In my case, the work goes down well in Germany – I feel they get what I'm trying to do (more than generally happens nearer home). Maybe that's because the work has taken so much from German literature. The reason doesn't have to be that direct, though. My Mexican translation got quite a good reaction too, and I was told that was because of the shared Catholic experience — not that my work could be accused of being overtly Catholic, but there is a fair bit of Catholic imagery or symbolism scattered through it, and a healthy awareness of death is never very far away. As one reviewer put it, it's Catholicism with the God taken out. My Dutch translation died a quick death though, and I'm not sure why. And I won't speak of the Slovakian translation, or the Croatian one that's about five years late.

It's obvious to any reader of your work that food and cooking are important to you. What was the last meal you prepared which you were really proud of?

I firmly believe there's a connection between poetry and cooking. The Poetry Society's café in London once asked a few of us to cook a meal from a particular country on the last Friday of a month, which we'd serve to sixteen people who showed up. I went for French, and did a Provençal garlic soup as a starter, followed by roast, pre-marinated loin of pork served with *choucroute braisée* (or sauerkraut cooked in the proper way that only happens in Alsace), and parsley new potatoes. I served an Alsace Pinot Gris with this. Afterwards, we had a selection of French cheese from a good deli, and finally a classic *tarte Normande aux pommes*, served with cream, and accompanied by a glass of Calvados. A journalist from *The Evening Standard* was there, and asked me what the connection between poetry and food was. Simple, I said. Importance of precision and clarity, and the need for good ingredients. Awareness of the weight of tradition and why a classic recipe produces a good result, and understanding of the principles that make a recipe work so one can be controlled in one's attempt to be innovative. He seemed happy with that and somewhere I have one cooking review to go with my many poetry reviews. The last meal I cooked that I was really pleased about was two weekends ago — a roast, pre-marinated loin of pork, again, served this time with a proper Provençal ratatouille (where each of the vegetables are tasted individually in the finished dish, which is a long way from the tasteless, soupy stew usually passed off as ratatouille).

FOUR POEMS
Matthew Sweeney

AN INVITATION TO DINNER

A sky blue envelope broached the letterbox,
bringing me an invitation (in cursive aquamarine
on a cream card) to a posh-sounding dinner
in a castle I'd never heard of in my part of town.
Yeah, right, I said, flinging the card on the floor
to observe that on the flip side it listed the menu.
I picked the card up again to appraise the fare.
Very interesting, I said to my stuffed hedgehog,
awaking his interest. For starters, either flash-fried
bear liver, or barbecued breast of flamingo.
The main course offered three possibilities, all
enticing. First, there was fillet of whale served
with steamed Tasmanian algae, next warthog curry
with wild forest rice, and finally, soft-shell coconut
implanted with desert vegetables and flowers.
Just the kind of menu that would make me drool.
How did they know? And what were they to me?
I looked at the address again – Castle Mada Rua.
Was it in red brick, then? How had I not noticed it –
unless it didn't exist, and this was an elaborate trap.
Some bad boys went to extreme lengths of ingenuity.
I got my thickest blue pen and wrote in big letters
on a blank page *Thank you, but I don't eat anymore.*
Then I enveloped it, and trudged to the Post Office
to put a stamp on a letter that would arrive nowhere,
before going back to fry an egg with too much cayenne.

PLUM SAKÉ
for Mary Donnelly and John Mee

The plum saké was left in a china carafe
with a design of purple flowers on it –
I found it on the low wall as I took the bin out.
One sip was enough to show how good it was
but who'd brought it here? I sat and drank,
slowly as the sunset, wanting more before
it was gone. I left the empty carafe there
and went in. I was imagining swooping in
a glider low over the ocean as I reclined
on the sofa, till the quiet ringing of a bell
brought me out into the garden to see the
carafe was full again. This time I continued
down the path to check if anyone was lurking –
any waiter or waitress in a black kimono, with
a bottle of saké, maybe brandishing a samurai
sword, with a red bowl for my severed head,
but all I met was a blind, three-legged dog.

I returned to the plum saké, and this time,
brought a chair out from the kitchen so I
could savour it better. Where could I buy
this nectar? Would I have to return to Japan?
I heard avian activity, and a long-tailed bird
with a black forehead landed on the gate.
I'd never seen one of these before. I sipped
my saké slowly as the rising moon, closing
my eyes to taste it better. Ages later I nipped in
to the little room and when I came back again
the carafe was full. I offered no complaint,
even raised my drink to toast the invisible
supplier, but I knew this was my last one,
I was not stupid. It was almost dark now,
an owl would soon join the bird on the gate.
I whistled a jagged early Tom Waits tune,
then glugged my plum saké down and went in.

STENCH

At first it was burnt toast — well, savagely
burnt toast, the kind where the bread is all black
and snaps into angry crumbs. No amount of
shaking the toaster would yield the offender,
nor would the smell depart. Next it was
rotten fish — no, rotten octopus (my nose
has always been a detective, unfortunately),
but where can one obtain fresh octopus in Cork?
And if you think that's bad, what about putrefying
minced pork, the kind I buy for Serbian meatballs —
had I stuck it in the fridge and forgotten about it?
There was also the ripe scent of dried ox-blood,
wafts of camel vomit, and a hint of donkey shit.
And last, *la pièce de résistance*, the unmistakable
stench of my own rotting corpse, even though
I was still above ground and able to smell it.
All these odours commingled, like a symphony.
Whoever had masterminded this, I had to take
my trilby off to him or her, and fling it out the door.
I also had to either move out or purchase a gas mask.
The clothes-peg on my nose had begun to hurt me,
the eau de cologne I'd drenched myself in was
evaporating. I felt like digging a hole in the lawn
and sticking my head in, though how that would help
was a good question. I was well beyond my last tether,
when the unexpected happened — the air took on
the pine-charged freshness of a Swedish sauna.
Coughing, I lay on the kitchen floor to digest all this.

THE TUBE

Golly, a nice man wants to put a tube
into my stomach, and his colleagues
are pleading with me to simply let him.

One woman sat by my bed holding
the harmless little tube, as if the sight
of it would make me say *Yes, stick it in.*

Instead, I continued to be noncompliant.
You might as well be holding a noose,
is what I said. The woman smiled and left.

I lay there and closed my eyes, imagining
all the nourishment that would go through
the tube, reversing my super weight loss.

I would now grow fat as a sumo wrestler,
or as the beer drinker I once was, back when
my illnesses lived in hypochondria county.

I could whizz up *boeuf bourguignon* to
baby food, or even thinner, and pump it in.
I could learn to forget what food tastes like.

They claim I could even still eat, with the tube
sticking out of me, but how could I revel in
a *Wiener Schnitzel* with that encumbrance?

No, that would be like eating on the train
to the black camp, this one with no skeletal
survivors liberated by a victorious militia.

I want to stay off that train as long as I can,
despite all the exhortations to board now.
I want to be myself till the last minute.

JIM GANNON, WITH DOG AND MODEL A, JANUARY 12, 1928
Greg Rappleye

He is standing in the Saco cold,
enough snow to say, Yes, this is winter,
and because we have a name and date
penciled faintly on the back, we can
be sure the glowering little man
is my grandfather, and is here almost
60 years-old. He looks older than this,
of course, looks tired, enervated,
angry with whomever is taking this
photograph along the lap-board rise
of a shabby mill-owned tenement.
Could the photo have been taken
by Armand Coté, Jim's Quebec
in-law, who had a Kodak Brownie,
wore a mothy beret, and worked
as lead-man over at Diamond Match?
Possibly, though it's hard to know—
the photographer is nowhere named,
and there is not a shadow of a body
washing forward, leaning to a lens,
to a focal point, shadow-grey across
the snowy drive. Jim stands in a wrinkled
shirt, a dark tie, half-Windsored
beneath an ill-fitting vest, his dress-pants
ballooning, a paper-boy's cap that covers
no doubt, a bald spot, Sunday shoes,
no jacket and no gloves. We also see two
skinny rear tyres, and the dark, down-curved
rumble-seat lid and convertible top
of a Model A Ford Roadster with
a 1928 Maine plate: 02-254.
This car cannot be Jim Gannon's.
Too old now to hustle the big looms,
he is only a ride-along teamster,

an over-aged delivery boy for the mill,
and could not afford a junky old car,
let alone a new Ford Roadster.
Nor would he buy kibble for a dog,
not one as hapless as this—
a mix of runty Boston Terrier
and shad-house mutt. It's a mystery
why Jim holds the dog's leash so
oddly—loop-handle in his left-hand
and the leash, stringing across his vest
to his right, where the cord is held
with only the index finger and thumb
of his right hand, and then down
to the sorry little dog—an affectation,
almost twee, as a desert saint might
be depicted in some Italian painting
from the early Renaissance,
holding a sprig of thyme or a tiny
bird's egg for all to see, by which
the viewer is to understand faith,
or the depth of God's love for a lonely
saint, surviving upon the merest trickle
of a nearby spring, upon bread-crusts
dropped miraculously by wheeling
desert birds. But here, we learn
only that the churlish man does not
like this dog. That the dog, tugging
against her leash, pulling sideways to
the scraggly wintered hedge, will yap
and yap, will distend her tongue
up and down against the choke of collar
and lead, and is unwilling to pose,
to still herself within the view finder,
because she
does not much like the man
who is holding her back, either, a man
so eager to be in his creaky stuffed chair,
out of the cold, away from the yappy dog
he hates and the car he can never afford,

that he will not smile and welcome us
into the frame. No, he says, Hurry up,
now, save the pity. Get an eyeful,
ya bastards, and turn the page.

Eigengrau
Colette Colfer

I climbed into time
to examine day and night
from a different angle,
slept whenever I felt like it,
ate breakfast at midnight
and dinner at dawn.

I stitched dreams into mornings,
left curtains open
through the spin of seasons
to watch the play of light and rain
on windows' changing easels.

I could see that the artist was right
when she said even time is light
and the absence of light is not blackness
it's eigengrau.

WE KEEP TRYING TO GET IT RIGHT
Jared Pearce

About a house away I heard this squirrel
Up the oak outside the pet groomers, chuffing
Like mad. I walked below him and looked
Across his land at nothing. He glanced down

At me, then again at the cooling sun, resuming
His song. I asked about his warning, a call to loving,
Thinking there must be some sorrow in his tuning, sure
His ardent clicking was ringing out some truth,

But it was only me making the making as he squatted
Like a prophet, a brazen nut, daring all to come,
Crack, eat the fleshy word and taste its alien tongue.

There was the gloaming, the icy air and frozen
Ground, there was space opening. There the chit
Chittering in the tree, and, walking away there, me.

MORNING
Vincent Francone

In the beginning is 6:00 AM

I get up, make coffee, have a sip.
The kitchen is lovely, dark, and deep,
cool and quiet—my wife's still asleep.

Between 7:00 and 7:20 I'm out
having a walk with Q.
who lets his dog-nose sway him

toward plants and bushes smelling
of more of the earth than yesterday
before the storm stirred what lives in dirt.

He keeps me out a bit too late.
I've got eggs to cook and I should shave
though I could get away with putting it off

and decide to—what's one more day?
My wife is up, her hair the focus
of the mirror. The radio is far too loud

and we're subject to the news.
The president has said something
indefensible, according to the interviewee.

*We really need political will, a broader
consensus, grass roots action,*
or something along those lines;

I'm only half attentive, thinking now
about the walk to the train, the dog's tremble:
he senses we're leaving and can't see why.

He gives his little collar a shake
to ask if there is some mistake
but I have a train to catch
and miles to go before I work.

TROIS PETITS TOURS
Scott Elder

The house is empty now
she unlatches the gate
feathers in the woodwork
smiles in cobwebs
a child's barrette on the floor

funny how objects cling to her touch
Jesus still hanging on the door
would she press her fingers to his cheek

the landscapes have vanished
a half heard tune
ferries back a few words

ainsi font font font
les petites marionettes

ah   she says
peering through a crack
it might only be a blackbird

an image hovers around the words
disappears

THE LETTERS IN A GIRL'S NAME
Michael Brown

From the outskirts of a town, say Darlington
for the sake of argument, you are perhaps
staring at the improbable satellites,
concave plates that call up and out
to an infinite space

or these backyards of a terrace block
which might yet peter-out to a park or become
the track of a man with a dog and a wife,
a scrap of land at the edge of a sky.

How you had wanted once to send such wands of light,
reach out from the dark page of yourself
to place those nine strange letters of your life.
From distance still I watch your untried hand
slur vowels, diphthongs mouthed in time
on your tongue and all the way down your right arm
to the pencil point pressed to its path,
a current to make something happen
from nothing: a name.
How you had shaped a line to call it out,
to find what it was to write, the crux
and spell of you, that first insight.

DESERT DAME
Emily Ellison

              your eyes
are prairie dogs
frolicking
under auburn
tresses,
           hiding behind
cacti silence
come night.
              I gorge myself
on agave
while the skeleton
dancing
atop your head
plays
           every 12-bar scale
he learned in fourth
grade
on the alto
       saxophone.
and so
you are blown,
a sunset against ocean-mirage,
a blues song I mistake
for burnt
       tumbleweeds
rolling my love
to water.
           in the wasteland
of your expression,
I am a hazel
of sand.

The Automatic
Mike Head

Put on my cotton underwear, but it was more like I was at the beach half-conscious of my body, half-conscious of the blue and splattering ocean... and my jeans came next, they were pungent with spring, and the many times I had walked down Washington Avenue, close to the kerb but closer to my dreams—in this salt-dusted town where the pedestrians rule, and they lead with a New England swagger—it's closer to a strut than a sway, but with all the elements of an object moving even if its legs weren't actually in stride... my socks came next... got them at EMS, and boy are they warm and comfortable! Like a dip in a pool with both stuffs of my stretching feet... as I choose my favourite t-shirt, I remember that it's like a slinking, permeable glove, to my chest and shoulders, to my heart that is picking up its rhythm... I am awake! And I reach for a collared, long-sleeve shirt—it's large enough for me to take what I need that day and give me full control of my swimming arms— they poke through each cuff...and my sweater is a wool one for the coarse Nor'easters, like the one now pulverizing the clapboards, making them rusty, and dry, and gray...my shoes are probably my favourite, how they soothe and hug my feet, with every bow I tie at their knotted ends...how I pace to and from the mirror, checking if my hair— which is basically non-existent—is straight enough to be viable (for the people that are basically non-existent... but ooze from under the door like a life) ... and how quickly it all comes off again! On that whim, of a whirl, of what's right...

GARDEN, HARVEST
Kelsey Dean

Mama's nails are lined with dirt.
Palms pink and milky from the pulling of
weeds: crabgrass, clover, dandelions.
Mama aches and smiles
at rosemary and lemon balm.

Sharp, insistent is the breaking
of a spinal column. The cord fraying,
notes of birdsong dissonant, dissolving;
soluble chemical drip in veins.
Mama's body a garden, more scars
ploughed in wine-dark furrows every season.
Mama's body a harvest, stripped
of flesh and tumours with scalpels, spades.

Mama halves peaches, pours oats.
Her fingers peel back stretches of skin
and wonder at the ease.
In the oven, fruit shrinks, bleeds,
and the taste of their tender unravelling
offers Mama seeds of comfort.

Opening Night, The Importance of Being Earnest, St James's Theatre, 1895

Jonathan Edwards

So there he is, one man there on the stage,
before a full and standing house, who called
for him before he came, who called for him,
and if you saw them clapping now you'd swear
they only just discovered they have hands
and mean to make the most of that. So there
he is, all dolled up, done up in a white,
white suit, one green carnation blooming there
in his lapel, smoking a cigarette
he's holding in one velvet scarlet glove
and waiting now for silence. His true love's
father, turned away at the stage door,

has left a large and festering bouquet
of vegetables with his name on, his lover's
in Algiers, where it's warm and easy
to pick up boys and there, in his white suit,
he's standing waiting these few minutes, moments
for silence, a few years for infamy.
Before he speaks now, before history,
that treadmill rushes in, let all of this
go on a little longer: one more drag
of his cigarette, another of those looks
that look on everywhere. Let them go on
applauding. Let him go on standing there.

LIKE A BAKED HEAD OF GARLIC,
George Angel

my singing spills over,
suppurates onto the hot surfaces
of where I am now.

Bluejays bundle
and break apart again,
as if needing momentary
nearness in mid-arc.

A sack of old flesh
squeezing out tears,
now and again.

Yes, this must be
what is called
the sentimental life!

TILTING
AR Dugan

These modern-day windmills
that don't mill anything
spin
so slowly

it's like they are doing
no work at all, but
here's what happens
when you get up close:

imagine a house fan
with 100-foot blades
that sound like cars
on a highway.

Imagine shadows passing
like super tankers
every 1-3 seconds,
killing and resurrecting the sun.

~

Wind power will save us,
they said, from ourselves.
Renewable energy, they said
and you think *That's good*

while you watch the blade tips
pass just overhead and
imagine the energy's potential
impacting your body. Imagine

what would happen
if the blades cut you apart
as they spin every 1-3 seconds.
They said *Dependence*

on foreign oil and fossil fuels.
They used words like
equality and *freedom.*
Every 1-3 seconds imagine

the potential of this cycle
that turns spinning
into death over and over
and never runs out of power.

Racing Through The Rain Forest, Glacier Bay
Travis Stephens

Summer in Southeast Alaska is lit,
night only a dimming,
even when it is raining, and it is raining
all the goddamn time.
 To the tourists huddled
along the rail as wet sparrows,
to the cruise ship fools and to the ones who rode the ferry in,
all wet, dressed for July somewhere,
 we remind them,
"It IS a rainforest."
 The Park Rangers in their Smokey outfits like to say,
"peri-glacial climate", meaning conducive to glaciers,
 Which is to say wet.
And cold.
Random college kids work at the Lodge and I
am in year two of this so I live in town.
Newly married, still poor, but glad to rent a
mossy A-frame off the main road.
My work is thirteen miles of gravel away,
 so I ride a borrowed three-wheeler,
fire it up at quarter to five.
Ride like a raven, banking
the turns, howling to the rain,
 waking anyone still sleeping in,
ANYONE STILL WAITING FOR THE SKY TO CLEAR.

The Top of Coom
Annette Skade

I walked myself into it, heedless
of the hill foreshortened by cloud,
even sketched it, above the stone circle,
rubbed my fingers in oilstick to mix
a thick grey and white. At the top
I'm bound fast, fog a wet rag in the mouth,
can't see a post a yard away on open land,
north and south all the same to me.

Low thud of boots on ground,
he splits the mist in front of my face,
a farmer, hat pulled down, old jumper,
padded waistcoat over wide shoulders.
He fixes me with an eye to strip paint.
"What brings you to the Top of Coom?"
chokes off my reply. "Have you your mobile?
I never walk the hill without."

He takes my silence for a no,
shakes his head, tells me I've no
business alone on the Top of Coom.
Then tips up his chin, sweeps
a long arm to cut a swathe
towards Glen Inchaquin. "Down straight.
If you go wrong or twist an ankle,
just shout. I'll hear you, this weather."

Cleopatra in the Flesh
Carolyn Oliver

At the Barbican, spring 2000

Our teachers said the actress, middle-aged, would strip
to her skin in the final act, and feeling quite mature
ourselves, we dressed in all our gawky regalia,
our curiosity cloaked as worldly nonchalance.

Except the teenaged elect among us. They conferred,
and when her capture came they left their seats, convinced
they could not look upon a queen's bare breasts,
her back, the soft meat of her thighs, and yet keep faith.

As if the stately edifice of her body were more perverse
than four acts' worth of a couple turning exquisite disaster.
As if we didn't tempt each other, shame each other, fully clothed.
As if we were not, all of us, tragedies in waiting.

When she dropped her robe, we who stayed saw her
as passengers in a ship tumbling far from the coast peer
through portholes, glimpsing a pale breaker a long way off
in the dark sea, a gasp of foam racing for the last shore.

How vulnerable we must have seemed to them that night
as they kept vigil in the cool quiet, their empty seats
gouged-out eyes. Unseen, we revealed ourselves. Gazed,
aching, at death laid bare, welcomed its warm lover's bite.

Southword Fiction
Chapbook Competition 2018

10,000 -15,000 word limit which can consist of a novella, a long short story, several short stories or a collection of flash fiction or a mix of stories and flash.

Stories can have been published previously in anthologies or in web or print journals, but not in a stand-alone publication by the author.

Two winning manuscripts will be selected, **Best International Entry** and **Best Irish Entry**. The winning chapbooks will be published and made available internationally through Amazon. Winning authors will receive advances of €250 euro each and twenty copies of their chapbook. The finished publications will be (along with preliminary pages) between 32-45 pages in length.

Deadline for receipt of entries is October 31st 2018. Winners will be announced by January 31st 2019. Winning chapbooks will be published by April 30th 2019.

There is a 25 euro entry fee. Entries will be accepted through *Southword's* submittable portal only. (Google 'Southword Submittable')
Nothing to identify the author must be included in the submitted manuscript document. All information about the contents' previous periodical publication etc. will not be needed until the manuscript is selected for publication.

Authors are advised that the finished publications will not include illustrations. All entries will be read and judged anonymously by Southword Editions editor Patrick Cotter.

Deadline October 31st 2018

The Frank O'Connor International Short Story Fellowship

The Munster Literature Centre is pleased to announce an initiative aimed at benefiting short story writers. The fellowship is made possible through the very generous sponsorship of Cork City Council. Named for one of Cork's most renowned writers it acknowledges the special place the short story form occupies in the cultural history and contemporary practice of the city.

The successful fellow would benefit from the prestige of receiving a highly competitive international literary award which will not only allow the candidate to spend time concentrating on their own work but also acquiring more experience in literary mentorship and teaching writing in an academic context. The successful candidate will have the opportunity to be inspired by living in one of Europe's oldest cities with a well-developed cultural infrastructure and a thriving literary community. The successful fellow would receive a monthly stipend of €2500, totalling €7,500 and self-catering accommodation. The costs of travel to and from Cork would also be covered.

The fellowship requires the author to reside in Cork for twelve weeks and find time to work on their own writing. The fellow would arrive in September and depart end of November. The fellow would contribute a public reading and a four-morning short story workshop to the Cork International Short Story Festival. During their twelve week stay they would provide a five-credit workshop with the creative writing department of University College Cork. Their mentoring duties would consist of devoting two hours each, per week, to two Cork writers over eight weeks (32 hours total). They will be welcomed into the literary and social life of the city where they will have the opportunity to network with resident established writers. They would present a farewell public reading at the Boole Library of University College Cork. The recipient would be a writer from outside Ireland of international standing.

Fellowship applications are invited from writers working in English from outside Ireland. Writers who work in another language whose work is freely available in English translation and who are fluent in English themselves are also welcome to apply.
The Short Story Fellow must have at least two full-length works of fiction published, of which at least one must be a short story collection. For full submission guidelines Google 'Southword Submittable' to find our submissions manager.

Deadline December 31st 2018

THE GREGORY O'DONOGHUE INTERNATIONAL POETRY COMPETITION 2018

Judge: Brian Turner

1st Prize:
- €1000
- a week's residency at the Tyrone Guthrie Centre
- paid travel expenses (up to €600) and four nights accommodation in Cork city during the Cork International Poetry Festival (March 27-30)
- publication in Southword 36 March 2019

2nd Prize €500 & publication in Southword 36

3rd Prize €250 & publication in Southword 36

Ten runners-up will be published in Southword 36
and receive €50 publication fee

Deadline for entries 30th November 2018

For full details on how to enter go to

www.munsterlit.ie

Astrid Alben's latest book is *Plainspeak*. Her poetry, essays, translations and reviews have appeared in *The Times Literary Supplement, Poetry Review, Poetry Ireland Review,* & elsewhere.

George Angel lives in Columbia where, under the name Mario Angel Quintero, he has published six poetry collections as well as three books of plays in Spanish.

Maria Isakova Bennett lives in Liverpool. Her pamphlet, *All of the Spaces,* was published by Eyewear.

Michael Brown lives in Cleveland, UK. His work has been published in *The Rialto, Butcher's Dog, Lighthouse Journal, Other Poetry, Crannóg, The Moth, Southword* and elsewhere.

Dean Browne lives in Cork. His poems have appeared in *Poetry, Crannóg, The Penny Dreadful* and elsewhere.

Colette Colfer lives in Waterford. She has been published in *Poetry Ireland Review, Skylight 47, The Poets' Republic* and elsewhere.

Lily Cook is an undergraduate student at Hampshire college., Amherst, Massachusetts.

Tomás De Faoite was born in Dowth, Ireland. He lives in The Netherlands. His second collection *Green Father* was published by Poezie-uitgeverij WEL.

Kit de Waal is a national of both Britain and Ireland. Her novel *My Name Is Leon* was Irish Book of the Year.

Kelsey Dean lives in Ann Arbor, Michigan. Her poems have appeared in *Cicada, Tincture, Blue Heron Review* and *NonBinary Review,* among others.

Danny Denton lives in Cork. Granta published his debut novel *The Earlie King & the Kid in Yellow* this year.

A R Dugan lives in Boston. His poetry can be seen or is forthcoming in a number of literary magazines and reviews, most recently *Salamander*.

Jonathan Edwards lives in Gwent, Wales. His first collection *My Family and Other Superheroes* (Seren), received the Costa Poetry Award.

Scott Elder lives in Auvergne, France. His collection *Part of the Dark* is published by Dempsey & Windle Publishing.

Emily Ellison is a first year MFA poet at Texas State University.

Vincent Francone lives in Chicago. His work has appeared in *Spectrum, Rhino, New City, The Oklahoma Review* and elsewhere.

Mike Head is from Cape Cod, Massachusetts. He has been published in *Four Ties Literary Review* and *Poetry Nook* . He has released an album of funk/rock/indie pop music called *Rouse.*

Julie Irigaray is based in London. She has been selected as one of the 50 Best New British and Irish Poets 2018 (Eyewear Publishing).

Rose Keating lives in Waterford. She is a recipient of the Séan Dunne Young Writers award.

Mercedes Lawry lives in Seattle. She has published two chapbooks, *There are Crows in My Blood* and *Happy Darkness*.

Deborah Levy is a British playwright, novelist, and poet. *Swimming Home* was shortlisted for the Booker Prize. *The Cost of Living: A Working Autobiography* was published this year.

Valerie Lutte lives in Cambridge, Massachusetts. Her stories have appeared in *Everyday Fiction, The Good Men Project, Prime Number Magazine,* and *The Rusty Nail,* among others.

Norman Minnick lives in Indianapolis. His second collection of poems, *Folly,* was published by Wind Publications.

Elisabeth Murawski lives in Alexandria, Virginia. *Heiress* is being published by Texas Review Press this autumn.

Louise Nealon received the 2017 Sean O'Faolain Short Story Prize.

Jared Pierce lives in Oskaloosa, Iowa. His debut collection of poems *The Annotated Murder of One* was published by Aubade Publishing this year.

Carolyn Oliver lives in Worcester, Massachusetts. Her poetry has appeared *FIELD, The Shallow Ends, The Greensboro Review, Booth, Gulf Stream* and elsewhere.

James O'Sullivan lives in Cork. *Courting Katie* (Salmon) is his most recent collection.

James Owens lives in Indiana and northern Ontario. His most recent book is *Mortalia* (FutureCycle Press, 2015).

Greg Rappleye lives in Michigan. His third book, *Figured Dark,* was published by University of Arkansas Press.

Penelope Shuttle lives in Cornwall, UK. Her eleventh collection, *Will You Walk a Little Faster,* Bloodaxe Books appeared in 2017.

Annette Skade lives in County Cork. Her first collection *Thimblerig* was published upon winning the Cork Literary Review Manuscript prize.

Breda Spaight lives in Limerick. She has been selected as one of the 50 Best New British and Irish Poets 2018 (Eyewear Publishing).

Travis Stephens lives in Malibu. He has been published in the *Upriver Anthology, NOTA, Stoneboat, Crosswinds Poetry Journal* and elsewhere.

Matthew Sweeney *see page 79*

Yoko Tawada writes in German and Japanese. Her novels include *Memoirs of a Polar Bear* and *The Emissary.*

Rachel Trezise is a Welsh author and a recipient of the Dylan Thomas Prize. *Cosmic Latte* is her latest book.

Simon Van Booy lives in New York. He is a recipient of the Frank O'Connor International Short Story Award. *The Sadness of Beautiful Things* is due out from Penguin later this year.

P.C. Vandall lives in British Columbia. She is the author of three collections of poetry including *Matrimonial Cake* (Red Dashboard).

HOW TO SUBMIT

Southword welcomes unsolicited submissions of original work in fiction and poetry during our open submission period January 1st to March 31st 2019. Work selected from this period will be published in *Southword 37* in September 2019. Submissions will be accepted through our submittable portal online.

For unsolicited work *Southword* will pay €40 per poem and €250 for a 3000 - 5000 word short story.

We welcome submissions of up to six poems in a single file or one short story no longer than 5000 words. We ask writers to make no more than one submission in a submitting period. Further instructions can be found on our submittable portal from January 1st.

Southword 36 will be published in March 2019 and will include winning and shortlisted poems from the Gregory O'Donoghue Poetry Competition, judged by US poet Brian Turner, as well as winning and shortlisted stories from the Sean O'Faolain Short Story Competition, judged by Irish novelist Paul McVeigh. The issue will also include commissioned poetry and prose non-fiction.

If *Southword* can garner enough subscribers we will publish three issues a year from 2020, with more space for unsolicited work.

Printed in Great Britain
by Amazon